No Pressure,
No Diamonds

"Teri Dillion's *No Pressure, No Diamonds* confronts the reader with a searching, well-written, and honest summons to remember both the fragility of the body and the tenacity of the soul. Through her personal inquiry, she asks each of us to consider how much we may ignore our final appointment with mortality and yet what we are called to develop whenever it makes its appearance. At "mid-life" she is at the end of life and offers to each reader the gift of Persephone's wisdom: someone who moves between worlds and brings messages from both. Her work is a gift to us."
—James Hollis, PhD, Jungian analyst and author of *Living Between Worlds: Finding Personal Resilience in Changing Times*

———

"In the form of this beautifully written, always loving and honest, sometimes humorous account of her soul's journey with serious illness, deeply informed by her Buddhist practice and body-informed archetypal therapy, Teri Dillion teaches by example and has given us a gift that will outlive her body. Moving and compelling for anyone who leaves the ranks of the 'temporarily immortal.'"
—Katy Butler, award-winning journalist and author of *Knocking on Heaven's Door* and *The Art of Dying*

———

"This book is a gift. Teri continues to serve as a therapist, spiritual seeker, and truth teller as she shares what it was like to come to terms with a shocking and debilitating terminal illness. Laying bare her own humanity, it felt as though I was being given an opportunity to deeply experience my own. Exposing her longing for an ever-elevated life, coupled with a belief it would always be

available, Teri drills down to her own heart. She takes us inward, inviting personal reflections about life's purpose and meaning. This book offers everything you hope a memoir might: capturing the nuances of a true, messy, rich, complicated, heart-breaking experience that is LIFE. I finished the book feeling humbled, inspired, wiser—and with a new definition of 'a life worth living.'"
—Ingrid Clayton, PhD, clinical psychologist and author of *Recovering Spirituality: Achieving Emotional Sobriety in your Spiritual Practice*

———

"This book is for *every* human. Dillion teaches us what true grace looks like when 'reality calls' and it's not what we wanted. Tragic, yet surprisingly light-hearted, this book is beautifully written—something we can all learn from."
—Amy B. Scher, author of *This Is How I Save My Life*

———

"As I read the first words of *No Pressure, No Diamonds,* I felt like Teri Dillion had reached into my chest and grabbed my heart. 'Here,' she seemed to say, 'this is where it matters.' I was utterly tenderized before finishing the first page. Sharing both her humor and her pain, Teri suggests no easy answers, but instead offers a pathway that may lead to being truly human. This is the real deal: a treasure that humbles, inspires, strengthens, and perhaps even awakens the reader."
—Karen Kissel Wegela, PhD, LP, author of *Contemplative Psychotherapy Essentials: Enriching Your Practice with Buddhist Psychology*

———

"Compelling and moving, you will be changed by reading this book. Teri invites us into the raw, honest, and searing reality of confronting the profound loss and deep grief of letting it all go. The reader journeys with her into the underworld as she reconciles with the karma-scorching process of fighting for one's life. Out of this fight, Teri emerges with a kind and gentle heart, a capacity to live and love freely and spaciously alongside the confines of her physical limitations and impending death. This book is for anyone interested in living with more surrender, acceptance, and gratitude for the simple acts of being and loving, no matter what the external circumstances present."
—Elizabeth A. Olson, PsyD, LCSW, CGP, owner of the Collective for Psychological Wellness

—

"Teri's book doesn't disappoint. It's compelling, drawing you in... and making you feel like you're right there with her as she navigates waters we can only imagine. I'm grateful to Teri for sharing these precious lessons with all of us."
—Brian Smith, author of *Grief 2 Growth: Planted, Not Buried: How to Survive and Thrive After Life's Greatest Challenges* and podcast host of Grief 2 Growth

No Pressure,

Mining for Gifts
in Illness & Loss

No Diamonds

Teri A. Dillion

Author's Note: This book is a work of non-fiction. In some passages my thought processes have been condensed for narrative flow, or I wrote to convey the underlying feeling tone more than exact dialogue.
In either case my memory is subjective and will differ from others'.
Some identifying details have been changed.

This book is not intended to substitute for psychotherapy or professional medical advice. If you think you could benefit from therapy, contact a licensed mental health professional.

First paperback edition November 2020

ISBN: 978-0-578-73688-4 (paperback)
ISBN: 978-0-578-79223-1 (ebook)

Book design by Christina Thiele
Editing by Chandika Devi
Proofreading by Laura Kincaid

Pomegranate Publishing

www.teridillion.com

*For all those enduring a squeeze
they aren't sure they'll survive*

And for John

"The formation of natural diamonds requires very high temperatures and pressures. These conditions occur in limited zones of Earth's mantle about 90 miles or more below the surface, where temperatures are at least 2000 degrees Fahrenheit... Diamonds formed and stored... are delivered to the surface during deep-source volcanic eruptions. These eruptions tear out pieces of the mantle and carry them rapidly to the surface." Hobart M. King, geology.com

"What is to give light must endure burning." Viktor Frankl

Contents

Introduction

There was the official disease I had, and then the disease I would come to identify as far more soul-crushing. The latter is a disease for which there is no twelve-step program, even though there are millions of us who fall prey. No hero doctor, charismatic guru, or revered shaman has a proven protocol for treatment. No pills or surgery will hasten the recovery, and no amount of visualization, affirmations, or positive thinking will herald its cure. Recovery from this disease requires an entirely different kind of medicine.

This disease of which I write—slippery devil that it is—is the disease of tidy answers.

But before I jump into the details of this malady and the path of healing, it feels only fair to offer a disclaimer about the story I'm about to tell. Be forewarned, dear reader:

1. It's not tidy
2. It doesn't truly provide answers, and
3. It ends with death.

I know, it's enough to make the best of us go off searching for something more satisfying like *Immortal Bliss in Seven Days*, or *Indestructible Platitudes*. But there's still some hope. Please don't despair. If I've done a decent job illuminating what I hope to in these pages, you might even be able to find something freshly redemptive about your own (occasionally) workable, (probably) mystifying, (undoubtedly) imperfect life and body reflected here; your life and body which will hopefully keep humming onward in relative ease for many, many years. That's because this book isn't so much written for the ill or the dying, though those of you inhabiting bodies of disrepair—*I see you*—might soon find yourself punching the air in satisfied cheer.

Instead, this book is about forging a path through the harmony and the heartbreak we are each privy to by virtue of being in human form; wading through the universal experience of loss, breakdown, and falling apart; and then finding a way to revision and reclaim that which remains meaningful, potent, and even sacred in our lives—*despite*, or even *because of*, the precarious state of our bodies. And for that reason, this book is also about the never-ending art of growing up.

But to explain how my own journey of recovery from tidy answers began—and which tidy answers I'm even recovering from—I first need to back up about four years, to what might be called the beginning of my own dark night. It all started with the *other* diagnosis. And while diagnoses happen to many of us in the course of our lives and the implications run the scale from ignorable to devastating, I just so happened to hit the jackpot of drama, the grand slam of misfortune, or as I'd soon learn some doctors call it, "the worst possible thing."

Out of nowhere and interrupting an otherwise beautiful Thursday morning, I was slapped with three uppercase initials that signified I was now victim to a rare, quickly debilitating neurological disease. It was the kind of disease which results in total paralysis—including the loss of one's voice and an assured countdown to respiratory failure—within a few years for nearly all who are diagnosed with it.

Ouch.

But wait. If this prognosis wasn't enough to violently shake my once-placid existence, the blows continued as my partner and I ended up losing our home, all our possessions, and an ungodly amount of money, all courtesy of an unfolding string of unexpected events in the months and years relating to the diagnosis. Not long after—because the remaining corners of my life also clamored to buckle into the great chasm—I was stripped of all remaining faith in my long-adored Buddhist teacher, our spiritual community splintered after revelations of abuse met critical mass, and the meaningful container from which to frame this life-shattering turn of events blew away like a Tibetan sand mandala that had met its fate.

Okay, ouch is an understatement.

Of course, I hadn't seen any of it coming. The day before the diagnosis—the day before the Earth first opened up and swallowed me whole, that is—I was so confident in the promising course of my future that increasing life satisfaction felt almost fated. I was thirty-five and at a beautiful resting point, relaxing into a well-curated adulthood, seemingly long before having to reckon with the threat of death or disease. I was growing accustomed to feeling competent and in control, after all; I had even cheekily joked about becoming a master of manifestation, well-armed with a type of plucky American exceptionalism that told me if I appeased the divine Powers That Be with my good intentions and earnest efforts, if I did my homework and ate organic and always wore the right shoes for the occasion, things would more or less work out. I believed there was some feel-good rhythm, some predictable cause and effect, some, *ahem*, simple answers to how life works. Cue the gods, or the mystics—or the quantum multitudes more commonly known as the universe—belly laughing.

Call it chance, or destiny, or the cunning cosmos wanting to poke a hole in my existential hubris, reality had other plans for my precious life. I was being schooled in the ancient lesson that most of us will learn eventually: that certain blessings (especially including our health) are safe to take for granted until the day they are suddenly, inexplicably, shockingly *not*.

My internal compass toward the sacred started spinning. It felt personal. It felt abusive. I wanted to send it all back. Of course, questions followed in the attempt to make sense out of the senseless. I wanted to know what had gone wrong in my life and body, and what to do about it; what my illness meant, what I needed to learn from it, and most importantly, how to heal the impossible. I wanted to be triumphant in my hero's journey; I wanted to manufacture a miracle. And I was prepared to use every ounce of will and wit I could muster to make it happen.

Yet beyond my personal devastation and demand for answers, something more measured inside—perhaps the occasionally objective psychotherapist, or the sober-minded Buddhist—quietly remembered difficulty and loss is just a part of the package accompanying the gamble of life on Earth. Welcome to the pain school, where reality retains ultimate license to swallow us whole without warning.

In the face of messy, mind-blowing, immediately uncontrollable realities, tidy answers have a funny way of oozing forth from well-meaning mouths. Such answers include "everything happens for a reason," or "there's a larger plan." They include "your circumstances are a reflection of your spirit/karma/consciousness," or "*anything* is healable with enough faith/meditation/microgreens." The "look on the bright side" answers can be used as a way to convince us to hurry up and relax, to stop feeling blown apart, as if #itsallgood, the universe only dishes out spiritual justice, and positive thinking cures everything.

On the more resigned end of the tidiness spectrum, conclusions sound more like, "shit just happens," or "it's all meaningless and random." And as I would soon learn regarding illnesses like mine, tidy answers include, "that condition is *never* healable, your life is a tragedy, and it's best you go on home and get ready to die." These answers are convenient when looking for a personal definition of an event—or the potential redemptive possibilities at hand—feels too threatening, early, exhausting, or futile.

But the thing about all these answers is that they are easy to throw toward *other* people's upended lives, and not always satisfying when it's our own life on the line. Something deep within us can feel abandoned by resignation *or* by platitude, as if our very souls are suffering insult. I certainly needed more nuance, to hold the complexity of ultimate workability alongside an admission of some degree of random unfairness.

Despite all the partial answers I came across along the way— the *whys* and *hows* and *what nows*—I was repeatedly graced with inspiration to dig deeper. Along the way, I would find that true nourishment only came after engaging with big questions, about faith, about cycles, about impermanence, about meaning-making and responsibility, about what it means to try and reknit that which is—or at least *feels*—torn apart. The type of questions that can best be answered in poetry, or prayer, or by painstakingly learning how to bear the unbearable, moment by tiny moment; and eventually, of how to live *with* a terminal condition instead of simply dying from it, because that's all any of us are ever doing anyway.

Eventually, I learned to question if I might have been entrusted with a body and circumstance capable of wearing down my rougher edges to reveal a clearer, wiser heart—a heart made rich by the willingness to consciously meet the details of embodied life, as suffocating as they often felt, and rest naked in my love and my grief. I questioned if I could trust in my own resilience and fortitude, regardless of the state of my body or circumstances, and even find an appreciation for life that was unfamiliar when things were going to plan. Just as a diamond is built after being subjected to incredible pressure, life-threatening circumstances provide us the opportunity—perhaps even the mandate—to bring our own creative intelligence to bear within the arc of our personal and relational evolution.

While my challenges were unique and specific to neurodegenerative illness, this is not simply a book about disease, its underlying factors, or its potential antidotes (even though you'll soon see I explored them all). It's about the redemptive power and the sobering complexity of relationships in the midst of illness, health, and loss. It's about the inside job of inhabiting and reflecting on a rapidly unraveling body and life, at times foolishly and at times courageously. It's as much about becoming as it is reckoning with death. I won't sugar-coat the experience of illness, but I *will* attempt to relay the timeless lessons and unexpected gifts that came along the way, some of which have been undeniably sweet.

"After enduring a harrowing journey and wanting to write about it," the saying goes, "write the book you wish you had had to see you through it." Even though as a licensed psychotherapist I had over a decade of training and experience working with people tossed about by trauma, torn apart by loss, left dizzy by change they weren't prepared to integrate, one might think I was well prepared for what I was ultimately called to go through. I was not. I'm not sure any amount of professional training or experience could have adequately prepared me, yet suddenly my interests in medicine and healing, initiation, post-traumatic growth, attachment theory, social psychology, mindfulness, spirituality, addiction recovery, developmental psychology, and neuroscience became prescient. Nonetheless, while I include these subjects here, I don't so much write as an expert; I write as an unsure human thrust into a harrowing reality I desperately wanted to understand, and I include reflections on diverse commentary which helps me tell—and make sense of—my story.

The process of writing this book has proven a salve to my spirit, an attempt at reclaiming both wholeness and mystery in pursuit of greater truths. By being open to difficult questions and possibilities more than the easy answers, I've found a certain medicine. I'd like nothing more than these questions to be healing for you too, if only in a small way, and for them to companion you through whatever you might be facing, which feels like more than you can face. If there are glimmers of potential poking through the rubble of your own life or body, may you notice them—and know that no matter how bad things might look, there remains more to be revealed. May you remember you're accompanied by the resilience and fortitude of your ancestors, tough cookies that they undoubtedly were until their last breaths. May you affirm how you were born hungry to meet this wild life, naturally accompanied by good measures of pain and grace, already carrying a courage and wisdom within you that the toughest passages may only help to illuminate.

I wish this for you with all my heart.

But first, back to my story.

PART I:

—

Hunger

1.

The Soul's Call

Two weeks prior to the day the Earth would crack open and swallow me whole, I sat still on a meditation cushion on the floor of my bedroom. The only sound in the house came through the open windows, as backyard crickets sang their soothing songs in ode to the warm, mid-spring evening. A flickering candle danced shadows across my little shrine while the sweet smell of incense slowly unfurled in the air.

Usually eager to pop up at the end of my meditation practice and resume more tangible tasks, on this evening after my timer signaled its permission for me to rise, I lingered. The space within me was unfamiliar—more still; almost pregnant. Something unnamable wanted to be discovered, perhaps even savored, and its peculiar beckon was compelling enough to delay the hundred other things I could be scrambling off to do.

So I sat and listened.

Slowly, a soft howl began to rise from deep within my belly, gaining volume and confidence as the moment stretched on. *Whoa.* After a sharp inhale, another howl followed, equally surprising in its intensity. *Whoa.* Then another pierced through. Then another. It was as if something ancient and powerful within had finally become untethered, like a wild band of horses breaking free of a too-small corral. *Whoosh.*

Before long, guttural waves began to fill the still room, shocking the witnessing walls, the hushed carpet, me, and likely my curious husband John upstairs, with whom I'd had an entirely pleasant and wail-free dinner just an hour before. Acting the faithful meditation student, I met the now-uncontainable uprising with curiosity. *Umm... what... could... this... be?*

Suddenly I was sobbing. I slid to the floor, where I would lie in a crumpled heap for the next hour, experiencing wave after wave of wailing cries. Never having been one to cry easily and rarely without obvious cause, these inexplicable tears felt strange and tender. It was as if my body itself was in mourning, independent of my conscious participation.

Grief! It's grief! I eventually realized. *But... why?* Life felt more fulfilling, settled, and workable than it ever had. What could I be grieving if there was nothing really lost? What did my body know that my mind, clever and analytical as it could occasionally be, did not?

——

Earlier that spring, I had attended a large conference in Manhattan designed for psychiatrists and psychotherapists and focused specifically on group leadership. During the last day, I found myself walking shyly into a workshop on Sensuality, Desire, and the Unconscious. Nodding my greeting to the few people I recognized from previous conferences, I took a seat in the large circle, hopeful I had made the right decision about which event to attend.

As part of the introduction, the presenters asked us forty or so participants to take turns stating which human archetype we currently felt like embodying and why. We could pick anyone, they said. "Let your imagination roam." And one by one the introductions began, with people choosing archetypes of comedians like Tina Fey or athletes like LeBron James or performers like Lady Gaga, saying they wished to be funny or creative or wickedly athletic.

Sensible, I thought. *But so contemporary, so literal, so… American. Can't you therapists fantasize?*

My turn soon came. Heart pounding as I stared into a large circle of well-educated strangers, I did my best to sound confident. "I'd like to be the Greek goddess Persephone," I said, pausing for dramatic effect. "Because she's able to walk between worlds."

The room lingered in stillness for a long moment, a moment seemingly more potent than what everyone else experienced. Eventually, the presenters nodded and thanked me for sharing, turning to the person next to me. My heart rate slowly returned to normal.

After an awkward ninety minutes of enforced milling and disclosing first-impression fantasies about the other participants *to* them—because therapists are often keen on self-torture in the name of training—we were released for lunch. At a table full of fellow Boulder therapists, I happened to sit by a graduate student from my alma mater who had also attended the same painful workshop. Soon after beginning a conversation, he said he found my archetype choice cool.

Ha! I thought. *That's right. And not even American.*

Of course, if he had been more curious, or bold, or even familiar with myth, he might have asked, "Hey, no offense, but… why idealize Persephone? Her situation was kinda less than ideal." He would have been correct, and this *might* have led to conversation at least slightly less awkward. But to be fair, my own curiosity about the deeper meaning of my chosen archetype was vague and hardly questioned. If I had been asked to explain the myth as we sat picking through our bland catered lunch, I might have meandered through a rough version of the following:

Persephone, adolescent daughter of the Greek goddess Demeter, was wandering alone in a meadow picking flowers one day. When Hades, God of the Underworld, spotted the innocent young beauty, he decided he must have her as his wife. With great rumbling, the ground split open and she tumbled below to his land of the dead. There, she became the queen of the dead and eventually learned how to minister to the various needs of her new people.

Demeter mourned her daughter's disappearance for months, and in her outrage and grief she stopped tending to her job as Goddess of the Harvest. As the crops withered, the people became hungry and pleaded with the gods, including Zeus, Persephone's father. Eventually, the gods took mercy on the humans and struck a deal with Hades: Persephone would return to the land of the living for half of each year. Demeter was satisfied to get her daughter back, even if only part-time. Her new joy allowed the crops to return in spring, heralding Persephone's return visit. And Persephone was tasked with bridging the worlds of the living and the dead. Well, okay.

Looking back I realize the actual implications of this plot—the dark, dreadful details of Persephone's newfound existence—must have been lost on me at the time of the conference. Who really wants to get abducted into Greek hell by the bad boy of the under-world anyway? Yes, being a queen has a certain pizzazz, especially if one's cape and boots are especially chic, though being queen of the dead kind of kills the glamour. Wasn't I tempting fate with this statement, giving a new definition to self-sabotage? I might as well have said I wanted to be Icarus, or even Job.

Of course, as a therapist I know us human-folk are prone to uttering strange, half-baked fantasies at times, including those which seem to come from nowhere and can shock anyone listening. But this was only one example among a growing number of stirrings for adventure I had begun feeling over that winter and spring. I had spontaneously confessed to the therapy group I participated in that I found myself wanting "unanticipated life-changing surprises" over the next few years, to which another wry group member reminded me to be careful what I wished for, considering life-changing surprises in adulthood are rarely the fun kind. We all laughed at this obvious truth. But nonetheless I persisted to hint toward a romantic longing in conversations with close friends, John, and my therapist. It lurked within me, passive but present, one step shy from being scribbled into my planner: "1) Optimize website; 2) Plan new veggie garden; 3) Fall through the Earth during sudden gobsmacking rumble with fate."

But by all outer appearances I should have felt complete. After having spent my twenties in a long series of sweet but ultimately ill-matched relationships, I had found artsy, soulful, sober John, also a therapist, and whose attention felt so good, and so easy. At the month-long meditation retreat where we were first seated side by side, I caught myself in impulse to lean over and stroke his back as if we were celebrating our fifty-year wedding anniversary instead of being acquainted only days prior. He felt like *home*. But in case the universe wouldn't trust us to grok the fatedness of our partnership on our own, she sent along literal pairs of hummingbirds, double rainbows, and uncanny synchronicities to nudge us along the way. *Okay, okay! Message received.*

Four years later we were married in a sweet, smallish outdoor ceremony and soon after bought our 1963 split-level home in a suburb near Boulder. We agreed the backyard hens would make a more-than-satisfying substitute to the requisite 1.5 children that we were supposed to want and spent our time plotting new work projects, weeding our uncontrollable new yard, tending our large collection of bicycles, feeding our friends, and trying to make sense of our shared Buddhist path.

In addition to this satisfying domestic life and freakishly compatible partnership, work was ever more creative. I had somehow emerged from working-class roots to build a meaningful self-directed career in teaching and private practice, and strung together a list of credentials behind my name like a long piece of fancy toilet paper stuck to my shoe. I was proud to have already transformed so many limiting messages and traumas of childhood, and in an increasing number of moments I was learning to feel comfortable in my own skin. We had enough income to eat out often, travel, and plan for a future of possibilities. My most enduring stress was how to choose between the four doctoral programs I was considering pursuing, just for kicks.

In short, I was wicked abundant in all the goods a privileged white gal in the suburbs could ask for. Conventionally speaking and by all appearances, I had already "arrived."

And yet those mysterious longings for a further surprise and change—as vague and romantic as they were—seemed to be tapping into a soul-level yearning of some sort. As mythologist Joseph Campbell might say, something in me was "hearing the call" for some deeper journey in my life. But what journey? And why now?

Reflecting on that lifetime ago—which in retrospect seems so stunningly innocent—I wonder if there's something archetypically prescient about such hunger. While it's possible that Persephone was just caught in the wrong meadow at the wrong moment, was pitched into the underworld against her will and had to make the best of it to ward off nihilism, it's also possible that something within her hungered for transformation. Perhaps she wanted to be tempered by an alchemical burning, to claim a greater strength and wisdom, to grow up. Maybe she wanted wholeness and was somehow willing, even if unconsciously, to sacrifice her comfort and security to find it. And after all, after years between the worlds, wouldn't Persephone eventually represent the perfect merging between light, heavenly spirit, and dark, earthy soul?

Perhaps in my longing I, too, was ready to confront myself in a new way; to worm my way through the deep, mineral-rich, unbehaved meeting with both the permeable boundaries of embodied life and the stark inevitability of death. To be swallowed whole by something fierce, sacred, intimate, and not entirely tidy; something I couldn't think, fake, or charm my way out of. And then, by some magic or everyday miracle, find a way to bring whatever I harvested back to my topside life.

Looking back, I can only see that my yearnings were barely conscious. Whether through my own unexamined hunger or the concordance of forces much bigger than me, I would get my adventure between the world of dark and the world of light, and between life and death. And by the time I lay crumpled on my bedroom floor, grieving something I couldn't yet understand, my body clearly knew what my mind did not: the shiny, promising path beneath my feet was already beginning to crumble.

PART II:

— • —

Tumbling

2.

Loss of Innocence

MAY 2016

The morning started with the kind of warm spring breeze which seems to herald a promise of general cheeriness from everyone, chattering squirrels included. My route had me weaving my bike along the Boulder Creek path around joggers, parents with strollers, and skateboarders. Wildflowers sprouted up the edges of the pavement in obstinate declaration: *Life returns!* I chuckled with giddy delight at how pleasant the whole scene was. Just one neurologist's appointment stood between me and the business of the approaching summer, and by this time the mysterious crying episode from two weeks prior was all but a distant whisper.

Despite the morning's good vibes, the appointment was not one I was looking forward to, an ominous cloud in an otherwise sunny day. I would have canceled it if I could do so without a nagging guilt, but I suspected it was a necessary annoyance to endure—especially since I wanted to finally put this ongoing medical mystery behind me. *But blessed be thy mystery.*

This "mystery"—otherwise known as unexplained symptoms—was tugging at the corners of my attention in an increasingly troubling manner. It had started the previous fall when I noticed myself fumbling while dressing. Bra straps and buttons became progressively more difficult to navigate; it was as if my fingers had stopped cooperating with my direction. At first it just seemed weird and only faintly worrisome. *Is it my imagination, or am I getting clumsy? Is this really a thing?* But over the months it slowly progressed to include my wrist, making cooking, doing dishes and typing a little more challenging. Unsure how seriously to take it, and wary of Western medicine based on past disillusionments, I decided to return to the chiropractor who had treated my scoliosis years prior. Since he had already helped my breathing and posture and overall well-being significantly, I thought maybe he could address this too. And sure enough, he ended up confidently reassuring me. "I see this all the time," he said, chuckling. "Nothing to worry about. Just come in twice a week, I'll straighten out your cervical spine, and you'll feel stronger in no time."

As much as I wanted to collude with my chiropractor's optimism, as the months wore on, having seen him faithfully three times a week, I could admit I wasn't getting stronger—*yet.* During a long-due but routine visit with my primary care doctor, I was surprised to learn she was not as dismissive of my new hand and arm weakness as I had expected. When she showed concern and urged me to call the number for the neurologist she wrote down, I remained unconvinced. *Pshaw. Totally overblown,* I reasoned. *I'm fine.* I would have taken my denial out for a beer if I could.

But thankfully I maintained just enough of a tether to reality to casually mention the referral to my therapist, Celia, weeks later. Much like any good therapist would, Celia promptly started giving me The Questions, plus The Head Tilt, plus The Tone, insinuating my nonchalant avoidance *meant* something, and what's more, we should probably talk about it—out loud, using words. Suddenly I remembered why I hate therapists. But apparently conventional medical advice is the kind of thing that adults are wise to relate to, and in more and more moments of my mid-thirties I was beginning to remember that I was, technically, an Adult.

Like any good misinformation campaign can do, the one I adopted from my chiropractor meant that by the time I finally first met with the much-better-qualified neurologist, me and denial were friends. During the exam, he tested my eyesight and sensory input, pressing on my fingers with pokey instruments: "Do you feel this?" *Yes.* "This?" *Yes.* "This?" *Yes.* Silence. When he started tapping on my elbows with the little rubber hammer, they jerked theatrically, suggesting strangely pronounced reflexes. He said nothing. As his tests confirmed my left-hand grip and arm weakness, with all other limbs appearing normal, his expression remained opaque and his tone even. Save for the one brief moment his voice swerved into concern when noting how thin my arms were, he didn't disabuse me of my stubborn optimism. I squelched the urge to explain how often my mom had apologized for bestowing me with my weeny arms. *It's genetic, dude. Chill.*

He recommended I return for something called an electromyography (EMG) test. The EMG, which I attended the next week, consisted of him sticking large pulsating needles into my back and left arm muscles to read the electrical activity of my nerve signals: a low-grade medieval shock torture. He then had the gall to tell me to get an MRI of my cervical spine, to which I outwardly agreed, and inwardly sighed. I never thought to ask him if this could be something serious, and he never mentioned that it might be.

Weeks later, as I was mechanically sucked headfirst into the confining MRI machine, my mindfulness skills went rogue. *Wait, how does that "calm" thing go again?* The loud beeps and crunches during the scan made my body jump, and I remembered how unexpected noises had recently begun to deliver a percussive shock inside my brain, sometimes sending me into a mini Tourette's-type swearing episode. Via a speaker in the machine, the medical tech asked me if I was okay. *Okay?*

"Yes!" I chirped. *I think... I hope?*

A week or two later, after the imaging center had sent the results to my neurologist, we arrive at today's appointment on this otherwise perfect spring morning.

———

After parking my bike and checking in at the front desk, I was promptly invited down the hall to the doctor. The appointment began with him taking me into a new room so we could go over the MRI results together on the computer. Unclear on what we were looking for, I assumed it was a good thing he was pointing out my cervical spine was basically normal, temporarily forgetting this was actually the opposite of good news. *Why does his voice sound weird?* I wondered, and *Why does he sound stressed?* He took me back in the other exam room and asked me to sit. He looked pained.

Taking a deep breath, he said, "I had hoped your husband would have been with you today." *Huh?* It had never occurred to me to bring John. The doctor had never stated this could be serious, and I knew it wasn't as if I could have some kind of cancer in my arm or along my spine. But now my stomach began to burn with fear. *Was this actually serious?* I held my breath.

With a tight expression, he continued. "I'm afraid to tell you that I believe you have a condition of amyotrophic lateral sclerosis."

My heart pounded. My stomach dropped. I suddenly had a certain numbness where my body used to be. Fever and freeze started to spread outward, from somewhere.

I stared, waiting for him to explain.

"Are you familiar with it? It's also known as Lou Gehrig's disease."

Something within became a little thick and fuzzy. It was as if a blanket suddenly wrapped around my brain, cushioning me from extra input. I had only half-formed thoughts. *What is…? Do people still…? How…? Does it… Multiple sclerosis? Will I… cane… wheelchair?* But I couldn't form these questions into words. I didn't know what to say, so I kept staring in his general direction. After a moment, my speechlessness began to include embarrassment.

Then the doctor explained there was a medication, Riluzole, that was quite expensive—like, a thousand dollars a month expensive—but if I began it immediately, it might extend my life a few months by improving lung function. He said he wasn't impressed by it or its side effects, but it was the only treatment option he knew of. I didn't yet understand why a few months would be a significant amount of time in the course of the disease, but the fact that this was the only option sounded bad.

My tears came despite me wanting to hide everything from this doctor, the doctor whose usefulness I was suddenly reassessing. Nonetheless I appeared deferential, as this is how one is meant to be with men in authority. "I'm sorry," I said, knowing the two or three tears sliding down my cheek might make him uncomfortable, suspecting it was my polite duty to protect him from my feelings, even now. He responded with a gentle "Of course," as if he were surprised I was holding it together at all.

He said although he was confident in the diagnosis, he'd like to send me to the university hospital in Denver so they could run more tests and I could get a second opinion. There might be clinical trials I could try to get into, he said, though his tone glumly communicated, "Don't get your hopes up because none of them will help." Somehow forgetting what he'd just said about the medication, I asked if the illness shortens people's lives. He nodded but said nothing more. Not really knowing what else to say but desperate for some hope, I asked, "Should I eat in some special way?" He shook his head and said it wouldn't matter. At this point I realized he was no longer looking me in the eye.

I then managed to stumble down the hall, mumble something at reception, and walk outside. With shaking hands, I tried to unlock my bike. *My 'cross bike! The bike I love!* Just twenty minutes before I had gotten off this same bike, enjoying my day and feeling positive about my future—a future full of growth and adventure and endless choices signaling agency and freedom. Now I sensed only a dark gaping hole where my bright future used to be.

———

Riding my bike was clearly not an option with wobbly legs, so I slowly started walking it toward the creek path. I fumbled with my phone to call John. *Answer! Please motherfucking answer!* His cheery, buoyant voicemail message greeted me. Trying to catch my breath, I left a string of indecipherable sentences signaling something was very, very wrong until I ran out of recording time. I kept walking. I wondered if I'd ever hear that pre-devastation cheer in his voice again.

I walked until I found a secluded spot on the creek set back from the path. It was there, sitting in the damp grass under the dappled light of the morning, where I first learned everything about my new diagnosis the doctor had not been willing to tell me.

As I scrolled through the search results on my phone, I read that ALS is a rare neurodegenerative disease with no known cause and no cure. Treatment is practically non-existent and really designed only for comfort. It mostly strikes those over forty-five, although occasionally people get diagnosed in their twenties or thirties. It's a process of progressive, inevitable motor neuron death, often starting in a limb and then quickly spreading to devour one's entire body. The mind is rarely affected. Late-stage patients would need a feeding tube and a breathing machine. Most live between two and five years after diagnosis. In that time, they become quadriplegic with no voice, eventually dying of suffocation once their lungs lose their strength. The death rate is 100%.

Well, *whoa*. I sat as fresh waves of tears started, thoroughly soaking each inch of the cloth handkerchief I kept in my bike panniers for emergencies. I fumbled out some texts to my brother Rob. I tried to send John thought waves to persuade him to call me sooner. *Joooohhhn… You want to call me… Call me right now…*

*Jooohhn… Pleeeeease…*While performing this desperate mental sorcery and assessing my available options for mopping up my snot and tears—*Would grass work? Could I use creek water somehow?*—I barely noticed the twenty-something man approaching me from behind. Once he was within a few feet he cooed, "What's a cute girl like you doing sitting alone on such a nice day?"

Startled, I looked up at him with my puffy, tear-stained face and noted he was serious about trying to casually pick me up. I conjured my most withering *can't-you-see-I-was-just-hit-by-a-bus, shitwit?* expression, and snorted loudly. He slunk away with his tail between his legs, throwing back a sarcastic comment only once he reached a safe distance. Momentarily distracted from my fresh trauma, I noted this would make a good story someday because I rarely got hit on. *May 12ᵗʰ, 2016. Nice day, my ass.*

———

Eventually John called back. He didn't understand my message and I had to break the news again. After explaining, he kept repeating, "What?", interspersed only with rounds of stunned silence. He said he would cancel his clients and meet me in the park near his work within a half hour. I would just have to ride the two miles along the creek path to get to him, a concrete task which felt somehow relieving in its simplicity. I called my office manager to have her cancel my day, suddenly blowing up my prized record of having late-cancelled a session only once so far in my career. After a couple more calls to my brother and an Al-Anon friend, both of whom reassured me that it wasn't necessary to panic before the second opinion, I pulled myself together enough to mount my bike.

During the trembly ride, I noted all the innocent people whose lives hadn't just been pulled from under them. There they were, in their own everyday life dramas, jogging their dogs or rollerblading with their headphones or strolling with friends, lost in conversation: "Get this! And then Kerry said...!"; "I don't know which job would be best..."; "... and then I'll have to take a red-eye flight to..." I'd listen to these snatches of conversation, knowing these people were completely unaware of their incredibly good fortune. By all appearances they still had a future, or at least a convincing illusion of one. I simultaneously envied them, prayed for them, and pitied their lack of awareness in their own vulnerability. This would quickly become a familiar flavor: envy.

When I met John in the downtown park, he threw down his bag to embrace me. After some moments together in silent trembling he choked out, "We'll get through this together. We'll get through this."

I nodded, my wet face buried in his chest. *I hope so. I hope so.*

———

The next day I put on a strong face and returned to work. I justified it with the argument that I needed to function, since I wouldn't know what to do with myself without some sort of human routine. After all, "doing" had always been more comfortable than "being," and I wasn't jazzed about having more time to *be* with this new reality. So, doing my best to tuck my new trauma into my pocket during the fifty-minute blocks with clients, I'd listen to them process frustrations about their probation officers or workaholic spouses or disappointing deck remodel. Their lives had barely changed, while mine had essentially been bombed overnight and they were none the wiser. During the ten-minute breaks between them, I'd write case notes while battling tears, telling myself that it's okay sometimes to be a crappy therapist who can only offer reflection from a hollow place of personal devastation.

John and I held a group conference call with my parents Debbie and Jerry in Phoenix later in the day, with my brother Rob joining from California. My folks were a little giddy and goofy at first, undoubtedly tipsy, not yet understanding the reason for the rare pleasure of having all us kids on the line at once. I took a deep breath, noticing John was holding his.

"So... I've been... Well, I went back to that neurologist, remember?" I said, trying to keep my voice steady.

With a bright voice, expecting resolution, Mom asked, "Yeah, what happened with that?"

Oh God. Should I draw this out? How the hell do I do this?

"Well, so... yesterday... he kinda diagnosed me with something called, um, ALS? It's... well, it's pretty bad."

I heard my father cursing in the background, away from the receiver. My mother, clearly shocked, just said, "Oh."

I'm sorry, I'm so sorry.

I continued: "Do you know about it?"

Dad, sighing: "Not really."

Mom: "No."

Their tones suggested otherwise.

I offered, "Yeah, it's... well... not good." We all paused. Struggling to keep the conversation going yet not knowing what to say, my mom squeaked out a weak series of "okays," and the beginnings of questions that couldn't quite form.

I wanted to do for them what the doctor had failed to do for me: provide a glimmer of hope and perspective. I continued, "But it might be a misdiagnosis. I'm getting a second opinion… it's too early to worry too much. There are still a lot of unknowns."

Rob stammered his way through a brotherly statement about coming together to support me. Our efforts were futile at best; until we all hung up, only heartbreak and confusion streamed through the line. John, speechless, hugged me from behind.

The days that followed were a hazy blur of calls, emails, and research. I couldn't eat much; John survived on black tea. Friends were confused when we broke the news. One even laughed, either from nervousness or because she assumed I must have been joking; I still don't know. Some would immediately reply with total confidence that it was a misdiagnosis since ALS was usually a disease of older men, and even then was rare. "How could you have that?" they'd ask. "You're so healthy. You don't have that."

I liked the thought, though it provided little relief. My stomach was now burning constantly, like when you go down that big roller-coaster drop, except this one just goes and goes and goes without pulling up again. And my other arm—the strong arm—suddenly began to weaken.

———

Throughout this week, I reflected on my lack of serious concern about my health up until the moment I was diagnosed, how I had so blindly assumed I wasn't a real candidate for a deadly disease. After all, these types of things happened to unlucky people, abstract people, older people, and, most importantly, *other* people. Maybe even people who were careless or sloppy about their health. If anyone ever had an "in" with the fates, I must, because I was so intentional about taking care of myself physically, emotionally, and spiritually. *Right?*

I exercised daily and went to yoga weekly. I smoked nothing and drank a couple beers every month or two. I hadn't eaten fast food since I'd been a teenager and rarely bought anything at the health food store more processed than, say, organic hummus. Once I realized my cravings for sweets had crossed the line into addiction, I'd been abstinent from sugar for almost a decade with the help of a twelve-step program. I'd been advancing steadily through a series of fairly intensive daily meditation practices under the tutelage of a respected Buddhist teacher. I went to my own therapy.

And I always said "please" and "thank you."

In my mind, all this meant one thing: I was good, *damnit.* I was "good" at respecting the literal and energetic laws of well-being, so it seemed obvious that life should be good to me in return. This was *me* after all, the center of my own special universe, and I hadn't seriously entertained the possibility of a major misfortune. Or, if a misfortune happened, I assumed it would be of the sort where I could get the treatment available to fix it, and the strength of my resolve and determination and wits and karma would carry me through. Problem conquered. No problem.

Oh dear.

Funny how these persistent magical thoughts had managed to continue unexamined even though I knew from working with clients from every walk of life that shit happens, to everyone, often at the worst possible times. They had persisted even though I fancied myself well versed on social-justice issues, and could readily acknowledge having white, able-bodied, middle-class, well-educated privilege and all the invisible handouts privilege offers—including a skewed estimation of one's ability and entitlement to control outcomes in one's favor. And they persisted even though I had thoroughly studied the Buddhist teachings on the nature of impermanence, where all things "good" and "bad" inevitably change, where "death comes swiftly and without warning."

Suddenly I realized I had long labored under the fuzzy assumption that my spiritual efforts and intentions would account for something—meaning an enormous slap of wake-me-up misfortune wouldn't be called for. It's notable that my teacher's own Tibetan teacher, Chögyam Trungpa Rinpoche, had taught all about the dangers of spiritual materialism, when we mistakenly believe that our spiritual practice and mindset should somehow save us from life's hard edges. I had always believed I understood this teaching. And I *had*—at least in theory. But once my illusion in a decently satisfying or predictable future got stripped from my hands, I realized I hadn't really gotten it like I could have. *Oh, so* this *is what he meant. Damn.*

Nonetheless, holding an abundance of socioeconomic privilege, some old-fashioned good luck, and perhaps even a smidge of youthful optimism had thus far insulated me from the harder edges of reality. It allowed me to maintain the "I'm good/clever/special enough to avoid a total shitstorm" belief, the very defense mechanism that many of us have *until* the unspeakable visits us, a way to distance ourselves from others' misfortune and maintain an illusion of superiority and outsized control. This made my new reality an especially insulting, confusing—and perhaps even due—wake-up call.

In a moment of desperation later in the week, I found myself at Barnes & Noble between work and home. Since books had always been my go-to pick-me-up whenever I was lost or overwhelmed, this seemed a natural place to end up. Trying to get some perspective that would buoy my spirits, I headed for the spirituality section, desperate for a loving reminder that things might still be okay in the big picture.

The first book that caught my attention was *On Life After Death* by Dr. Elisabeth Kübler-Ross, the infamous grief-stages guru. Claiming to provide "a message of hope to the living," I thought this little book might offer some necessary soothing. I picked it up. *Please*, I internally pleaded with whatever kind unseen forces might be listening. *Give me the message I most need to get me through this. I need perspective… please…*

I opened the book to a random page and read as Dr. Kübler-Ross explained how she liked to remind her cancer patients that things could always be worse, lest they get lost in self-pity. For example, they could have something called ALS.

Oh God… no. My face suddenly prickled with that strange freezing heat I'd felt in the doctor's office. She proceeded to explain the ways in which ALS would be a much more terrible fate than anything they could dream of with mere cancer. I then skimmed through. *Eloquent words… insulting words… horrible words. Blah, blah, blah…* Fuzziness kicked up.

Of course, I didn't yet know how often I'd hear variations of this idea about ALS being "the worst possible thing" from doctors;

"my biggest nightmare" from friends; or "I'd just kill myself" from strangers in the months and years to come. I did know, however, this wasn't exactly the loving reassurance I had prayed for in the moment.

Score another *whoosh* down the steep roller coaster in my belly. I put the book down with trembling hands and walked out of the store, wondering what kind of cruel universe could think these things up. With tears in my eyes as I ducked into my car, the questions that had been pounding in my head over the week suddenly broke louder: *Why me? Why now? Is this just a massively unfunny mistake? Could I have prevented this? Is there truly a loving Source of Divinity, and if so, what the bloody fuck is it good for?*

As I stabbed the ignition button with an angry finger, I resolved to never again buy into the woo-woo myth of a compassionate and meaningful universe. I decided I'd been duped all along by a wishful, feel-good illusion of grace. *Fool*, I thought. *I was simply lucky until now.*

3.

The Art of Unraveling

A year before the diagnosis, my meditation teacher Reginald "Reggie" Ray, whom I had by that point studied under intensively for a decade, had hinted toward something in my headspace that needed a certain, well, *piercing*. It was during a week-long retreat volunteering as his attendant, an admittedly difficult role—even more so when held on top of my paid position as his executive assistant. Since I maintained a full caseload of clients while tending to him, the irony that I chose such a demanding "vacation" from work was not lost on me.

As a Vajrayana teacher and scholar of Tibetan Buddhism, Reggie was known for having a remarkable intellect and cutting insight. Many of us students repeatedly clamored for and feared his feedback whether inside or out of formal interviews. Feared, because his behavior and moods were unpredictable and could suddenly turn wrathful; clamored for, because his students were often 1) growth seekers wanting perspective and opportunity to build devotion to wisdom; and/or 2) craving the high from being love-bombed with an occasionally tender, supportive, compassionate presence—a real-deal teacher.

Those of us charged with responding to his moment-by-moment needs and whims were unofficially tasked with buffering the inevitable tension this dynamic created between him and any co-teachers, staff, and students. At one point when leaving a staff meeting filled with a certain fresh drama, he stopped, turned to me, and asked, "Are you okay?" Caught off guard, I said yes, ignoring my anxiety. "Your face is… tight. You look stressed." Continuing to stare at me, or what seemed to be *through* me, he said, essentially, "It's all okay. You gotta relax. Big time," referring, presumably, to the Ultimate Perfection of the Whole Cosmic Shebang.

With retrospect, my stress made perfect sense for the situation, which felt high stakes—as scenarios mixing hierarchical, interpersonal, and psycho-spiritual factors have a funny way of doing. But at the time, I could only note that Reggie's insinuation about my psycho-emotional state was not unfamiliar feedback—I had repeatedly been told by friends and mentors that I was probably working too hard on too many projects and could stand to slow down, unwind a little, maybe even lighten up. Despite knowing this type of advice can be dished out to women in a veiled effort to shame their ambition or engagement, I sensed it held a certain truth in my case. Perhaps they all knew work and goal-directed activity—the most socially rewarded fixes we modern people have to try to anesthetize against anxiety or emptiness—comprised my favorite unaddressed addiction. But coming from Reggie, this brief interaction had, indeed, pierced through something in me. *Did I need to slow down and relax further, and if so, how? If my meditation practice wasn't doing it, if my daily walks and my own therapy weren't doing it, what would?* I thought of this interaction often in the many months that followed, and especially once the full extent of my illness—or, as I'd learn some people would call illness, a "profound inner unbalance"—was made conscious.

————

In the months before my diagnosis, I had been satisfied that I was approaching the completion of a set of practices known as *Ngöndro*, a term related to the Vajrayana path of Tibetan Buddhism. Ngöndro requires many hundreds of hours of contemplative practices which build on each other, including physical prostrations, mantras, and visualizations, all meant to wear away the various egoic blind spots we humans come equipped with which shield us from the brilliant, interconnected, groundless nature of reality.

Or, at least, that's how Ngöndro had been marketed to me by Reggie. And, in many ways, the path delivered. I slowly softened, became less guarded, more present. By this point I had been doing these practices for five of the ten years I'd spent in Reggie's sangha, and would soon graduate to a new level of teachings and commitment. It felt like we were all doing something special, something sacred—something no one else was doing. I wanted to be "all in."

Admittedly, though I had been a diligent student all along and felt increasingly equipped to meet life on life's terms, I lacked confidence in the outcome of my efforts. I suspected I wasn't really getting whatever insight I was supposed to be getting and likely needed to effort even harder toward locating the calm, luminous awareness that was supposedly already within me. But more importantly, I wanted more of what Reggie jokingly once called cosmic orgasms, those moments in meditation where so much breathtaking beauty of reality is revealed that one can't help but gasp in ecstasy. Despite Reggie's reminders that cosmic orgasms were unnecessary and sometimes even distracting to a true understanding of the path, I wasn't convinced. I'd sit in retreats during special teaching sessions, trying hard to will myself to relax enough to let go, and, little surprise, it didn't work. Instead, I often felt completely, utterly ordinary, catching myself wondering when the practice session would end so I could go for a walk or make some toast. People around me would be gasping and sighing—like John, who can start vibrating just by feeling the energetic intensity of, say, a fluorescent light bulb—all gobsmacked by glimpses of the crystalline nature of space. But, far from any cosmic orgasms, I wasn't even making it to first base with the universe.

I repeatedly confessed these prudish sins to Reggie and any other senior practitioners who would listen. "I'm just not getting it! I'm really… just, basic," I'd pronounce, hoping they would take pity on me and give me the special missing instruction which would shore up my embarrassing gaps in spiritual insight. Instead they would all assure me I was, in fact, getting it, insofar as there was an "it" to "get." Yet my spiritual imposter syndrome persisted, with me assuming I had fooled them all into vastly overestimating my meditative abilities.

Still, though I carried these insecurities and doubts as constant companions, I felt committed to the process and was planning to steamroll ahead until I finished the required practices to make it to the next milestone. I'd practice for two or more hours most days, and I knew some inner alchemy was taking place, even if it was painfully slow. So I figured though I may forever be a remedial student, at least I was making some tidbit of progress, if through no other method than my stubborn willingness just to sit down each day and follow instructions as best I could.

Days after diagnosis, Reggie tried to support me by scheduling a meeting to help me modify a practice to my new situation. His suggestion to meditate four hours a day felt like a good idea until day two, when it started to feel like punishment more than support. Something in me knew that my era of earnest striving had been irrevocably punctured. Pushing for realization now seemed useless. Why would I need a physical prostration to teach me how to surrender, when my faltering body and life would do it simply fine? In some respects, I suspected my journey of waking up had only just begun.

———

Later that week, I lay next to John, grateful to have made it to the mattress. My second-opinion appointment had yet to arrive, affording me a sliver of hopeful comfort that this whole nightmare could soon dissolve. But this hope was buttressed by fear, what-ifs, and problem-solving fantasies, now a rapidly paced news scroll underlying every waking moment. This see-saw swinging between imagined grim or redemptive futures was naturally crippling, rendering slumber my new best friend, a forgiving respite in the landslide of unknowns.

I pulled the covers up as far as I could. Perhaps I had taken a bath before bed, or perhaps I was simply exhausted; either way, I relaxed effortlessly, nursing the gradual surrender into sweet, sweet unconsciousness. And yet something different than sleep lay waiting for me.

As I lay there on my back, semi-conscious, John starting to snore next to me, I gradually became aware of a vivid, full body experience of falling.

Down…

down…

down.

I fell for a good twenty seconds or so—*down, down, down*—enough time to observe clenching all my muscles in fear, desperate to stop the wild powerlessness. It's as if I was physically arguing with gravity, hoping if I resisted strongly enough I could prevent the whole experience, and, further, prevent the eventual violent smack against the hard earth.

Yet halfway into this fall, without conscious intention, something within just relaxed. My muscles slackened as I realized I could simply exhale with my whole body instead of holding my breath. I was still falling, but my fall became easy, as if just a floating sensation that happened to be quick and downward through space. My body surrendered to a gravitational process over which I had no control.

And then it stopped. I didn't hit the ground—the whole falling sensation just evaporated as quickly as it had started, even if the relaxation itself felt timeless. Once again, I became just a person lying in bed, a bit stunned, trying to grapple with what had just happened. While it's possible this event was a natural byproduct of a nervous system on the fritz, I knew it wasn't so mechanical; it felt unusually foreign and important, like something I would be wise to remember. It was as if something outside of me—or perhaps deep within me—had offered a teaching so my body could learn to relax into what I was facing with a certain grace. Not quite a cosmic orgasm, but powerful nonetheless.

———

First, I lost my grip on small, physical abilities. As the weeks wore on and my fingers became weaker, I lost my beloved ability to type with speed and had to start clumsily pecking at the keyboard instead. I lost the strength to button my pants, so I wore my shirts long and loose and made note of the need to check my zipper frequently in case it was sneaking downward. Not able to get the requisite grip on lamp switches, I learned to turn lights off by unplugging at the socket instead. Unable to clasp my bra behind my back, I began to clasp it ahead of time and slip it over my head. anxious about stretching the straps out prematurely. A moment later I remembered this anxiety was petty in light of what I was facing. *Oh, right… Priorities.*

I started using adaptive tools. The most powerful one was a plastic key grip with a long handle which allowed me to get more torque when turning door locks I encountered. I used it with abandon until the day I turned it with so much vigor that I broke the key off in the lock to the only entrance to the suite holding my office and ten others, meaning I couldn't get in, and neither could anyone else. Once I contacted the building manager, omitting the detail of the tool I had been using as I explained what had happened, he teased me about my superhuman arm strength. *Oh buddy*, I thought. *If you only knew.*

Meanwhile I contemplated what it might mean if I lost my ability to ride a bike, a beloved activity I'd enjoyed nearly daily for my full adulthood. Or hike in the foothills. Or make a sandwich. Or wash my hair. Or type an email. Such simple activities of life I had long taken for granted. Who would I be without them? The loss of my voice, or my ability to walk at all, were not yet in the realm of something I cared to imagine.

Until I had a better understanding of how—and how much—to disclose my situation to my clients, I strove to hide my emotional shakiness and growing physical disability. *They are doing good work,* I thought. *I shouldn't interfere in their process by having them focus on my unknowns. They are paying me to be available to them.* Since I was holding on to the possibility of misdiagnosis or, even better, spontaneous reversal of my symptoms, I decided it was too early to break any news. *Just... hold... on.*

But even though my own pain lay in the air unspoken, unacknowledged yet undoubtedly affecting the psychic space my clients and I shared, I found myself surprisingly present. Newly humbled by the stunning vulnerability of being human, I could now better transmit, *Life hurts, yes. And I can meet you in your bewilderment. Let's behold this big vista together.*

A number of my clients spontaneously began exploring their own themes of sorrow, and although I hadn't changed my advertising, I began getting an unusual number of calls from prospective clients primarily struggling with grief. It's as if I had gained new credentials through loss, and those out there needing a particular medicine—someone with the capacity to understand an abyss—were drawn to me through some mysterious radar, asking me to witness with them.

———

Throughout the tear-stained haze of summer, well-intentioned friends and family would approach clucking, "How are you?" in messages, in calls, while standing at our front door. Sometimes they would wear puppy-dog eyes and sometimes they were strangely chirpy; either way I mostly hated the open-ended question, especially if they weren't offering their own soul on a platter for me to see first. *You're really going to ask me that? How the hell do you think I am? Flipping fantastic, having a ripe ol' time?* Instead, I'd remind myself it wouldn't be wise to become a fiery dragon and singe my support system with displaced rage when they uttered something between a mindless greeting and a fair question.

Of course, this most basic of questions left me with a difficult choice: pretending I was okay (which many people would prefer), saying "I don't really want to talk about it" (which some would be offended by), or again attempting to describe the emotional complexities of facing a wicked scenario (which a handful could show up for, though it often left me exhausted). Middle ground was hard to find.

Mostly I felt cosmically alone, outcast from the natural order of things, assuming no one would understand. It would take years to learn that this perception, while true in the relative sense that my experience was unique to me, was ultimately a sick person's rookie error. Plenty of people had faced the threat of their own death and/or significant disability. I just didn't know why it had to be me, now, in this way.

Meanwhile, throughout the process of letting go of my physical abilities and the unraveling of my emotional rules, it became increasingly clear that hour by hour, moment by moment, I could fight and tighten or I could relax into the free fall. The only thing I couldn't do was stop it.

When fighting, I could focus on the unfairness of everything I was losing my grip on. I could obsessively plot my escape. I could analyze if ALS showed up to force me to slow down, disallowing further movement and activity through a literal paralysis; after all, I knew metaphysical matriarch Louise Hay had a tidy explanation for how it all makes sense symbolically.

Or I could gently call myself back when tempted by self-blame and panic, and remember to simply breathe. I could practice finding a more forgiving toehold to where I already was, establishing my place on the cliff by noticing small, everyday moments of redemption and workability within the life I still very much had: the gentle affection in John's eyes when he'd kiss me goodbye in the morning; the afternoon sun streaming through our glass door to my favorite chair and warming my bare skin; the sweet smell of the tiger lilies someone left on our counter; the purity of laughter between friends that can only be found after an intense cry. I could lose myself in soulful songs of hope by Patty Griffin or Sam Cooke, playing them over and over until I felt something tight inside slowly loosening. For brief moments, I could just be human, luxuriating in the sensual, simple pleasures of the present moment. For brief moments, I could relax into letting go.

4.
Seductive
Illusion of Triumph

SUMMER 2016

When my second-opinion appointment arrived, I was better armed. Meaning, I had John with me, because I had by now learned a lesson about going to see neurologists without a backup nervous system to provide support.

The ninety-minute drive down toward the teaching hospital on the eastern edge of Denver was mostly silent, each of us trying to grapple with the potential outcome of this appointment. The tension in the car was thick in the way tension becomes during a fight, but we weren't fighting; we were quietly terrified. He gently held my hand resting over my knee, occasionally stealing glances to see if I was still breathing.

Once we arrived in the mega-complex of the hospital and found a spot in the right parking lot, we turned to each other for a sigh and a pep talk. I said all the things I wanted John to say to me; things I wanted to be true.

"This hospital and everything that happens within it is just one paradigm reflecting one set of beliefs about reality."

John nodded.

"And we don't have to hold total allegiance to this version of reality as the ultimate authority on the wild, nuanced, sacred thing known as my health."

"That's right," he said.

"Fundamentally, disease is an illusion and nothing that is said or done here regarding my body can in any way tarnish my true nature as eternal, indestructible awareness."

"Truth."

"And lastly, but most importantly, no matter how this appointment goes, we will be getting lunch at Larkburger on the way home. Right?"

John liked this burger gospel best and offered a clear, emphatic *yes* to prove it. Having established that much, we were ready to enter.

The labyrinthine hospital was intimidating, as if designed to short-circuit the navigational instincts of the uninitiated. It was crowded. Staff and patients moved in all possible directions, the former efficiently, the latter appearing lost: the perfect metaphor for life with illness. Us patients and our loved ones—spanning a continuum of age, hue, and shape—wandered along, each housed within our uniquely vulnerable bodies. The basic pain of mortality felt undeniable. My conflicted heart swelled.

Once we arrived at the right floor for neurology, we made our way to the check-in counter, got the requisite clipboard, and landed in the joined vinyl chairs of the waiting area. I began on the paperwork, mostly only skimming, absently signing my privacy and money and perhaps dignity away. When finished, I resumed the only useful thing to do with nervous attention at a hospital: people-watching. John was already engrossed, or perhaps only lost in his own drama of thought, absently gazing outward.

Before long, a white couple a little older than us came to check-in at neurology; she, well dressed and looking weary, and he, paralyzed, dressed in sweats, and operating an electric wheelchair through tiny hand movements. My stomach sank as I wondered if this would be John and me within a couple years.

Eventually in the midst of my staring, I locked eyes with the man. Looking away quickly was futile; the damage had already been done. In that second, he managed to transmit exactly what I didn't want to see: he was completely lucid, and also completely torn down after being held hostage in a body that had betrayed him. His eyes clearly housed an intelligence and presence and all but screamed, *I am trapped, and yes it's as bad as you think.* Or—that's at least what my frightened eyes saw. He provided a mirror for my own terror, which I couldn't yet see past.

Before long, we were called back to meet the neurologist. She carried a straightforward competence which didn't exclude warm humor, which put John and I both a bit at ease. We discussed my symptoms, and she did a manual exam on my limbs and sensory inputs, not unlike the first neurologist but much more in depth. By the end, she said she'd like to do a brain MRI and a number of labs to be sure, but... *wait for it...* "I strongly suspect you do, in fact, have ALS."

Damn. *Damn.*

This time, I was more prepared with questions to ask.

"What about alternative treatments? Like chelation? Other detox methods?"

"Too early to get experimental," she said. "Those could be dangerous."

"What about methods to oxygenate the blood? I have these journal articles about treatments that have helped others with ALS, and you have the machines in this hospital."

"I'd be extremely uncomfortable with recommending that. Not enough data to support it yet."

"Okay, are there any treatments you *would* recommend?"

"Not at this point... not really. Let's gather more information."

I nodded quietly. John nodded quietly. Inside, I screamed. *Just give me a paper to sign! What more do I have to lose? Isn't it time to throw everything at it? Don't I have a right to try?* I greeted the now familiar icy/hot feeling in my chest. I don't know what John greeted.

Moments later we found ourselves sitting in another, smaller office down the hall, this time facing the occupational therapist. Somehow, I agreed to the neurologist's recommendation for a meeting with the OT, "to make a connection," but now that the connection was being made, I was less sure of its timeliness. After brief introductions, seemingly oblivious to my shell-shocked stare, the OT was already diving into showing off various arm braces I could start using. I noted she must be fresh out of grad school, twenty-five, tops. Her eager cheer told me she felt safely removed from our situation, and I imagined being viewed as just another patient/challenge to practice her new craft on as she began what would be her long and satisfying career.

Though I didn't *want* to hate her, suddenly I *did* hate her—and every health provider like her whose life wasn't on the line but who still felt qualified to advise us on how to relate to my condition. So naturally I started to have a tearful meltdown just as she began launching into the incredible benefits of adaptive can openers. But John noticed my I'm-about-to-fucking-lose-it face, and, acting the good partner that he is, announced our sudden need to depart. He grabbed my bag and new ugly arm brace, and firmly shepherded me into the hallway so I might start breathing again.

After swallowing the urge to scream and collapse on the floor over the injustice that was my life, he walked me through the hospital labyrinth to locate the lab, at which I needed to offer my arm for fourteen vials of blood. Then, thankfully, *finally*, we were free to leave.

An hour later, over our lunch of grass-fed, bun-free burgers and baked sweet potato fries—a very Boulder-type naughty splurge meal but barely nutritious enough to not spike my newly intensified health guilt—I felt myself recovering from the morning's overwhelm. We began to discuss a separate plan, one no one had even discussed at the hospital: The Find-Out-Why-I'm-Sick Plan. If conventional medicine held no hope, no curiosity in what health issues might have been related, *and* no interest in experimenting with treatments, we'd have to look elsewhere for answers.

"Let's do what it takes to give you a fighting chance," said John.

The only trick now, I said, is figuring out what the heck that might be.

Of course, doing what any sensible millennial faced with an unfathomable challenge would do, I googled how to fix it. Using every possible combination of phrases that might hold the magic key to freedom, I searched and scrolled and clicked over the following weeks, staring at my laptop for hours until my eyes were glassy and my neck was wooden. On the few occasions when John suggested I could take a little break, I gave his idea the most polite eyeroll possible, murmured, "Just another moment," and then continued for another hour or two. Who needs feelings when you can keep shaking an ever-changing Magic 8-Ball of information instead?

Traveling down the endless rabbit holes the Internet supplies, I came across abundant theories and tales about recovering from any and all illnesses considered incurable. There were juice cleanses and water fasts; parasite purges and coffee enemas; prayer circles and master energy healers. Some people claimed healing terminal conditions by totally forgiving others who had hurt them, and some said they did it after finally getting the nerve to tell others where they could shove it. Completely contradictory advice abounded on diet, exercise, and which treatments should be prioritized for neurological disease. Pseudoscience and anecdote were generous. I didn't really care; desperation fostered openness.

I read doctors: Bernie Siegel's *Love, Medicine and Miracles*; Gabor Maté's *When the Body Says No*; Lissa Rankin's *Mind Over Medicine*. Over breakfast I listened to interviews with Bruce Lipton and metaphysical types who lectured on the science of belief and how, oftentimes, healing needed to take place in the mind before the body. I heard and read and reread the theory that nearly all disease is simply some combination of deficiency or toxicity in the body, and once you figure out which combination it is and properly address it, healing is just a matter of time.

More relevant to me, however, was finding the stories of a few dozen people who specifically reversed ALS and got their lives back. This wasn't supposed to be possible; I had by now even seen an informational poster published by the ALS Association with the friendly reminder, "ALS is always fatal," lest anyone newly diagnosed forget to devolve into utter hopelessness about it. It's officially known as Game Over, Mission Impossible, Life Sucks and Then You Die. But sure enough, reversals existed, many of which were tracked and verified by Dr. Richard Bedlack, a respected neurologist and head of Duke University's ALS Clinic. The reversals who didn't make it into prestigious journal articles created lengthy websites featuring their stories of partial or full recoveries.

The common factors to most of the documented reversals, at least that I could surmise, seemed to be careful nutritional supplementation and/or properly identifying and removing one or more toxic elements. Those elements usually consisted of some stew of heavy metals, chemicals, or pharmaceuticals, mycotoxins from mold exposure, and chronic bacterial, fungal, or viral infections that have somehow evaded a depressed immune system and invaded the central nervous system. Many of these cases suggested that even if there was some unknown genetic susceptibility in patients, it was an environmental factor that ultimately nudged them over the cliff.

And by now I knew amyotrophic (Greek for "no muscle nourishment") lateral (portion of spinal cord) sclerosis (scarring) is simply a description for a pattern of progressive motor neuron death, and diagnosis is only the result of ruling out other conditions.

There is no direct test for it. I found theories which suggested there are many potential routes to the same destination of "ALS," that it seems a certain series of levers in the body get tipped off in a certain sequence, causing a cascade of degenerative processes which are very difficult to reverse. And yet, the people who do recover after proper diagnosis—in some instances, quite dramatically—provide evidence that reversal is something the human body is capable of under the right conditions. Or, at least, that *some* human bodies are, for whatever reason. It's also worth noting that few of the people who recovered got help from conventional medicine; they mostly did so through enormous leaps of faith, research, and experimentation at their own expense.

So, like Velma facing a life or death mystery with only a gigantic digital Scooby Gang (i.e. the Internet) to help out, I added a new layer of determination over the panic. These stories of people like me recovering their health held promising clues, and if someone else could do it, that meant I could too, *right?* I tasked myself with figuring out how a 35-year-old with a healthy lifestyle gets a deadly, non-genetic disease anyway—because, presumably, knowing the *why* could lead to the *how* of fixing it. And since by now all the neurologist-ordered labwork had ruled out other easily recognizable conditions, I knew I was on my own for finding answers—a project which was now consuming all my extra energy and attention. Lucky for me, I had an idea where to start. I lived in Boulder, after all, the Rocky Mountain capital of all things woo.

Prior to diagnosis, I had already experimented with alternative modalities to address an array of chronic symptoms I had long carried—symptoms that I was, for the first time, starting to piece together. Some health problems had been going on since my early twenties, though subtle enough to ignore at first: slow recovery after exercise, feeling perpetually hungry despite eating three large meals plus snacks every day, out of whack hormones, funky digestion, constant bloating, intermittent fatigue. Over the years with visits to acupuncturists and naturopaths I was encouraged to drop birth control pills and start eating meat again, and after doing so my symptoms gradually improved. But I knew traditional Chinese medicine and naturopathic methods for locating the root cause of illness were most likely woefully inadequate for the raging health catastrophe I was now facing. And patience was a luxury I could not afford. So when a trustworthy friend gave me the phone number for a medical intuitive in Florida who apparently had a reputation for uncanny extrasensory accuracy, I was already intrigued. Though I found scant information about her on the Internet, I reasoned it was a good sign she got her business only through word of mouth. I called and asked her assistant for the next available appointment. Compared to endless shot-in-the-dark medical tests—whether through Western medicine or otherwise—one phone call seemed like a smoking deal if it provided a useful lead to follow.

On the day the appointment arrived weeks later, I found myself sprawled on the bed in the darkness of our guest room, feeling glum. In the window of time between making the appointment and its arrival, and after the many long days of discouraging research about my condition, I was skeptical that the call would amount to much. But as instructed, I dialed the intuitive's number at the agreed-upon time. After explaining the very basics of my age, the diagnosis, and my search for answers, she went to work. It took less than five minutes for her to speak up with her findings:

"It looks like you have Lyme disease. It's in your brain. You've probably been infected for about twenty years."

No… Effing… Way.

"Do you remember having something like a really bad flu as a teenager?"

"Uh… Not really?" *But I don't remember a lot of that time…*

"It looks like you have a high amount of heavy metals… In my experience, this is a fairly common issue in people with chronic Lyme. You need to get those out."The good news," she continued, "is that it looks like you could respond well to treatment once you find a doctor who specializes in Lyme."

"Wow." *Wow.* "So is the ALS diagnosis even correct?"I asked.

"Let me see."Long pause."Hmmm… it's not clear. I want to be clear on this, but I'm not getting an answer… I'm seeing Western medicine is still very confused about what ALS even is."

Well, yeah.

She continued. "But it's clear to me that no matter how it's labeled, it's the Lyme and the metals causing your symptoms. If it were me, I'd find the best doctor possible who specializes in this. You should begin to notice improvement within six months of strong treatment."

I hung up the phone with a small flutter of excitement. *Lyme disease! I'd love love love Lyme disease! Best. Thing. Ever.*

———

In a chance encounter with a new friend just weeks before, she also suggested the Lyme possibility. She said the symptoms of chronic Lyme are varied and can include severe nervous system involvement—like what's seen in MS or ALS. At the time I had thanked her for the suggestion but was doubtful about its plausibility. Even though I had been bitten by hundreds of ticks in the woods of Northern California while growing up, I didn't yet know that region had been teeming with Lyme infections by the 1980s.

But now, I thought back to those tick bites. I considered all the weird symptoms I had been battling off and on for over a decade. Could Lyme be the common cause? *Yes, please.* The whole idea was even providing the faintest hint of synchronicity.

When I shared the intuitive's findings with John later that day, he showed cautious optimism and said we should look into it. Over the following days I'd soon realize some of my friends were more skeptical; one exclaimed that she wouldn't give the idea credence because she heard that chronic Lyme disease doesn't exist. I'd soon learn that much of the problem with even getting properly diagnosed with Lyme disease stemmed from political factors and competing narratives in the medical community about its testability, prevalence, and severity. But when another friend suggested I contact her acupuncturist in Denver, whose accuracy for diagnosis of infection was supposedly unparalleled—even if unconventional—I jumped at the chance. I was Velma following clues after all, and I found what might be the right trail, listening to the clues as they came to me. And this seemed to be a wonderfully promising trail at that.

A couple weeks later, I found myself on a doorstep of a modest Depression-era stucco home in West Denver. As a well-known practitioner in the local chronic illness community, Claudia provides acupuncture and autonomic response testing—considered by many to be a superior form of muscle testing—treatment protocols out of her home office. When she opened the door, I saw she was roughly the age of my mother, attractive and kind-looking. She greeted me warmly yet without extra chatting and ushered me back to her treatment room.

During the brief consult we had at her desk, I explained my symptoms in detail, as well as the doctors' findings. She held her breath for a moment. As the gravity of my prognosis rightly turned on an internal alarm, I noticed a slight quiver rippling through her. She said, with hesitation in her voice, "Let's just see what we find."

I climbed onto the treatment table as instructed and lay back to gaze at the ceiling. Claudia's setup included hundreds of vials of bacterial, fungal, parasitic, and viral samples. Swiftly and confidently, she went to work, testing me by tugging on the arm I extended above. By holding various remedies and testing the muscle responses, the thinking goes, one can "talk" directly with the body to find out what pathogens are present and which remedies would effectively strengthen its ability to resist them. She also held a sensor of some kind to my various organs to identify where the infection might be concentrated. Though skeptical about muscle testing in general, I was willing to go along to see what she found.

Within ten minutes, she said, "Teri, notice this?" while tugging on my arm. "I am testing you for Borrelia, the Lyme bacteria." When she held the sensor to my head and along my spine, I could barely hold my arm up. When she held it to other organs, I was suddenly strong again. This suggested the bacteria was primarily partying in my central nervous system. My reservations about muscle testing wobbled; my body was undeniably responding to something in her vials.

She continued to test for a few minutes, and then had me sit up so we could discuss treatment. She knew of a number of herbal and homeopathic remedies which tested effective against the strains of bacteria found and estimated treatment would take about six months. *Hmmm… same as what the intuitive said.*

I asked, "You mean I don't have to worry about writing my obituary yet?" She smiled broadly and shook her head.

After loading me up with tinctures and pills which she placed in a neat paper bag, she told me to return in a month. "You need to go slowly. You might get really sick from the bacterial die-off, which could overwhelm your organs. Call me with any questions."

I thanked her through tears.

———

Once back in my car, I hesitated before starting the engine. My body was trembling with excitement, yet I still wondered if I was truly in the clear. Could it be so easy? Some herbs and supplements for a number of months, some flu-like healing responses, and I would be free from this nightmare? I couldn't conceptualize how it would make any sense for Western medicine to be so clueless about such a high-stakes misdiagnosis. And in the haze of diagnostic trauma, I didn't want to overthink it.

During the ninety-minute drive home through rush-hour traffic, I put my phone on speaker and dialed my parents to share the good news. My mother had hesitation in her voice as she asked question after question about what these findings meant; questions I couldn't really answer. Meanwhile, my father was celebrating in the background, coming on the line occasionally to say he knew all along I'd be fine. "Thatta girl, sugar!" he triumphantly shouted.

By the time I got home and checked my email, Dad had sent me Mungo Jerry's "In the Summertime" music video. I imagined his goofy dance moves and exaggerated facial expressions that had always delighted me as a child, and as I watched these 1970s musicians with epic facial hair play their song, I did a few subtle dance moves myself.

But the real dancing would break out in another month, after Claudia's findings were confirmed by a blood test. The confirmation came through IGeneX—known in the tick-borne disease world as one of the most reputable and sensitive labs in the country—showing that my blood sample was unarguably positive with the Borrelia antibodies meeting both CDC and in-house standards for evidence of active infection. This was extra validating; I now knew such unequivocal results were a rare jackpot, the kind which would be difficult for even Lyme-skeptical doctors to argue with. *Double winner!* The naturopath who I'd seen for the blood draw called and left an excited message on my voicemail: "Teri, with these results, it's clear your symptoms are definitely due to Lyme disease!"

Once my symptoms were reframed into a treatable category with a clear cause, I felt my hope returning in earnest. John and I celebrated with many extended periods of googly-eyed chuckling, and I texted ten of my favorite people announcing that my chances of recovery just increased a hundredfold, which felt a fair estimation. As the barrage of exclamation-filled responses rolled in, I fantasized about what to do with my new lease on life. *So I know now what it means to visit the underworld, and even better—to find the rope that'll pull me back to the living.*

Sweet, sweet unknowingness.

5.
Punches and Kisses

SUMMER–FALL 2016

Much as I wanted my recovery to be easy and soft, I was not completely seduced by the optimism of the acupuncturist. Shortly after beginning her herbal Lyme protocol, I called Denver's only "Lyme literate" MD who took insurance to try to make an appointment. I knew if allopathic doctors thought I was headed for death, and meanwhile I continued to lose the use of my hands, I needed the most serious healthcare we could afford. The receptionist told me the waitlist was six months and she could only put me on the cancelation list.

"Um, do you know the severity of ALS? You sure you can't bump me up?" I asked desperately.

"No, sorry," she replied in a flat, impatient tone. "We see many very ill patients. And if you miss the call for an earlier slot due to cancelation, we'll give it to the next patient."

Through gritted teeth I asked to be placed on the list, programming the clinic's number into my phone under the name, "LYME DR. PICK UP!!!!" For the next five months I would panic in a mad dash every time the phone rang.

By this time I had started to explore the political realities that shaped Lyme treatment and diagnosis in more depth. I read that certain outspoken doctors on the Infectious Disease Society of America (IDSA) tick-borne disease panel—especially the ones with the most chance to benefit from cherry-picking the research on Borrelia due to insurance-company consulting jobs, vaccine-development contracts, and other conflicts of interest—had done a top-notch job of muddling public awareness about the virulence and chronicity of tick-borne disease. Unfortunately, this panel dictated the education and treatment protocols for infectious disease (ID) doctors and clinics throughout the country.

Nonetheless, and against the good advice of more seasoned Lyme patients I was befriending online, I looked up the number of the Boulder County Infectious Diseases Center. The receptionist who answered my call politely listened to my explanation of my situation, test results, and request for an appointment. After I finished speaking, she said, "I'm sorry, but the doctors here do not believe in chronic Lyme disease, so we will not be giving you an appointment."

"What?" I gasped.

She repeated herself. "The doctors here don't believe that exists."

Hello, rage.

In my best attempt at a take-me-seriously voice, I shakily spit back, "That's ridiculous. So your doctors haven't seen all the open-sourced, peer-reviewed journal articles which give loads of evidence about how spirochetal bacterial infection can persist well beyond a month of standard treatment? And considering so many of us never even get the standard treatment once newly infected, does that mean the infection just disappears on its own? If so, why would we ever need treatment in the first place? Furthermore, not 'believing' in the existence and virulence of a complex, multifactorial disease that even the CDC officially recognizes with at least 300,000 reported new cases a year is equivalent to an oncologist saying they don't 'believe' in, say, the ability of breast cancer to persist or reoccur once treated for a brief period. In other words, stunningly ignorant." (Actually, I said half that, and filled the rest in later that day in my fantasy thought bubble.)

She politely replied, "I can give you a referral to a counselor to discuss your symptoms."

Really, I am losing the use of my hands, and you think I just need counseling? You clearly give my psychosomatic superpowers much more credit than they deserve.

I hung up in disgust.

Barricades to treatment continued. Neurologist number one, who first diagnosed me with ALS, had by now ignored three of my messages requesting a call back to discuss my Lyme test results. Neurologist number two, in Denver, admitted she didn't know how to properly interpret the test, so she referred me to the hospital's ID department. Feeling stubborn, and figuring the Denver doctors would surely be more informed than the Boulder ones, I made the appointment after Cigna reassured me it would be covered by my insurance plan. But once the day came to meet with the ID doctor weeks later, I understood why I had been played the fool. In that twenty-minute appointment—for which I made a three-hour round-trip drive—the ID doctor did three things: 1) Receive me while quivering and defensive like she was prepared for a fight, offering a sloppy manual exam in which my hands and arms were newly renamed "strong"; 2) Told me Lyme "couldn't possibly" be causing the symptoms of my ALS (that is, the same ALS which the whole medical system basically agreed had cause unknown), *despite* the positive blood-test results (therefore she would not test further or treat me for it); and 3) Render yet another "in network" appointment useless—even though it wouldn't ultimately stop Cigna insurance from charging me $750 for enduring it, somehow losing memory of the promise of a much more affordable copay. *Breathe, Teri. Effin breathe. And vote for socialized medicine.*

This poor excuse for medical care wasn't personal, even if having my life on the line sure made it feel that way. In the coming months I would come across story after story of patients like me with serious neurological symptoms experiencing variations of the same roadblocks to tick-borne infections treatment throughout the country. But it would take a couple more years before Lyme patients got organized and class-action lawsuits alleging conflict of interests, racketeering, and corruption by the Infectious Disease Society of America started rolling in.

——

Meanwhile, as summer turned toward fall, I willingly tried anything that might offer me a leg-up on recovery. In addition to the herbal Lyme treatment, I dabbled in hypnotherapy, endured acupuncture, and swallowed loads of nutritional supplements. I allowed a herbalist to burn a top layer of my upper arm to then apply "kambo" frog medicine into the wound to try to get me to purge, thereby forcing a massive detox; it only made me sweat and left me with a strange tattoo. I studied *A Course in Miracles* through a local discussion group, trying to make the notion that "there is no order of difficulty of miracles" palatable. I accepted in-person and distance energy healings, wherein I was repeatedly informed my recovery was imminent. For a week or two I even let a DVD teach me tai chi in our dining room, stumbling through the poses which required good balance—which, to my dismay, was every single one of them.

Some of these activities were doing some sort of energetic voodoo that was helpful on a certain level; if nothing else, I was becoming a self-made expert (and critic) of alternative healing methods. But physically, the results of my efforts were slow to non-existent as the months wore on. Though praying to see some small improvement in my strength or energy, I instead witnessed myself lose function in a methodical way, as if my body were a machine programmed to power down gradually. My arms got weaker, my gait became less steady, pills were getting hard to swallow, and to my horror, my voice was beginning to buckle with quickening frequency, signaling a weakening set of vocal cords.

There's no way around it: life was getting rough. No amount of feel-good tricks were making that reality go away. My body itself had become an emotional minefield, and focusing on its functioning only spiraled my fear. *Screw presence,* I thought. *I want out.* I needed distraction, so I unilaterally developed an important agenda for our household.

By early fall, Operation: Guilt Husband into Cat Adoption had been months in the making. I knew it was a long shot since John was allergic, but I was determined and wasn't going to be deterred by practical details. I had even begun forwarding him articles about low-allergy breeds in hope that he'd eventually cave through my persistent eagerness. Finally, it worked. He gave me the affirmative nod on a Saturday afternoon, agreeing we could begin our search. I responded with awkward hand clapping and shouts of triumphant glee. Within an hour of his newfound willingness to add to our family, I asked him to join me in the backyard.

Standing on our patchy grass under our towering cottonwood tree, I grabbed his warm hands while speaking the following plea aloud: "Dear universe: if there's a feline creature of some sort out there that needs a loving home, whose soul energy matches our soul energy, and who could bring as much healing to us as we could to them, please send said being to us quickly and easily. Thank you. Amen."

John nodded his approval with a grin and shared an "Amen." He already knew that a similar prayer spoken aloud by me daily for a few weeks before we met had been uncanny in its coinciding with his appearance into my life, so he tolerated my conversations with the generic divine.

We went back inside and busied ourselves. Within two hours, I got an email from a friend with the simple message, "You should check out this cat." A handsome young lap-hungry "mama's boy" from the local rescue society needed a new home. As a short-haired Russian Blue, he was a low-allergy breed. He would require a home free from macho men, scary dogs, or wild children. I knew immediately he was The One for Me—*ahem*, Us.

Within a week we introduced him to our household. After a shy day hiding in the closet, he crawled out and gradually began his signature chainsaw purring and roly-poly floor dance that pleaded for petting. His silver coat was so soft and inviting that it felt natural to drop everything and submit to his furry seduction. I was in love, and so was John.

His previous human, whom legend had it he helped cuddle back to health from a serious illness, had given him the name Pinot Grigio. We felt this name would be an unfortunate mouthful to yell to the neighborhood if he ever got lost. Fortunately, a few weeks prior I'd had a dream where I was given an elegantly wrapped gift named "Anupalaya." Upon waking I researched the meaning of the unfamiliar word, which turned out to be Sanskrit for "protection" or, shortened to Anu, meant "alongside." Over the coming months, newly donned Anu healed his skittishness with strangers and provided us entertaining furry distraction. Most importantly, he seemed to be living proof that prayers still had power. Or *some* prayers at least.

—

The Anu excitement carried us through fall with welcome distraction. Meanwhile it was undeniable that the herbal Lyme treatments still weren't helping to stop the forward march of my disability, and I knew unless soon halted, I would have to close my private practice. I'd already parked my commuter bike in the garage, and driving to work was becoming increasingly sketchy with my spastic reflexes. Once at work, and because my hands were starting to atrophy from the weakness of my fingers, I had to force myself to stop gesturing and drawing attention to them as I naturally would. My gait had become more awkward and wooden, especially if I was cold or stressed, so I consciously practiced calming techniques when escorting clients to my office lest I start to emulate C3PO's stiff robot shuffle.

In November, weeks before I was finally scheduled to meet with the Lyme doctor, I found myself on a call with my wise friend Melody. She listened to my justifications for continuing to see clients: how hard I had worked to build my perfect career, and how I was good at what I did; how my treatment costs were adding up; how I only had my longstanding clients left, which happened to be the ones I enjoyed working with the most. After humoring me for a few minutes, she took a deep breath and finally stated it plainly: "Teri, you really should not be working."

Gulp. "You think?"

She continued, "Don't you need every ounce of healing energy for yourself? Don't you deserve that?"

These words hit hard—*So clear! So practical!*—but not hard enough to agree on the spot.

Over the following couple days, though, I reflected on the refusal to close my practice due to the myriad unknowns which accompanied the Lyme diagnosis. But it wasn't until I became conscious of the absurdity of one lurking question—*Don't my clients need me?*—that I really got it. Exactly zero of my clients were facing a threat of similar caliber, and it's not as if Boulder didn't have ten decent therapists to choose from on every square block. Perhaps I wasn't as indispensable as my professional ego wanted to believe. Perhaps instead of their actual needs, it was *my* attachment to feeling needed that kept me from letting go.

In between seeing clients one afternoon, I admitted I was tired of supporting the mental health of others. I no longer had the energy to downplay my growing disability in order to keep stubbornly pushing forward. If I viewed my ceasing to work as a temporary sabbatical to focus on myself and adequately address my health as opposed to outright retirement, I could swallow it. So I said aloud, "Okay, universe. If you want to support me to stop working for now, you gotta somehow send us enough money to cover at least a two-month break from my income. I'll take that as a sign. Uh… thanks." I noted that the atmospheric calm that always seemed to show up when I prayed sincerely, even if clumsily, infused the office.

The next day, as John and I were doing our post-workday puttering around the house before dinner, I heard him gasp while opening the mail at our dining room table. "Uh, Teri?" he called.

Not knowing if this was a good or bad yell, I trotted over, holding my breath as I read over his shoulder. A friend had sent us a greeting card, accompanied by a check. The card said simply, *Teri & John, Go on a second honeymoon, or use this for whatever you need. Xoxo.* The check was written with a figure just over what I would have made in two months of work. He gave me a wild look. Heart pounding, I began to explain, "Ohmygod… Um, I asked for that… that's… because I asked."

That was it; I had made a deal with the cosmos and knew better than to back out after she showed her hand. I would wind down my practice, refer my clients out, empty my office, and turn in my key.

By late November, the long-awaited appointment with the Denver Lyme clinic arrived. John and I sat in the waiting room with nervous excitement about my finally getting adequate treatment for the infection. We were soon surprised to learn that because the waitlist was so long, filled with hundreds of desperate chronically ill patients, I *still* would not be seeing the doctor yet. Nonetheless, the prescribing nurse I was assigned to instead was warm but no-nonsense and ready to get to business. "Why were you on the waitlist so long in your condition?" she asked, incredulous. "You should've gotten in here within weeks of first calling!" John and I shared a look of exasperation. He would later share it took everything he had to not start yelling.

After getting loaded up with an array of prescriptions and new clinical diagnoses of neuroborreliosis and other tick-borne infections (Bartonella, Babesia, Mycoplasma), we returned home hopeful I'd start seeing some results soon after starting the antibiotics.

But of course that was not to be. As the weeks wore on with my new regimen, the forward march of my disability continued unabated. Because I had by now stopped working, I had little to do but track my body closely. Meanwhile, I began using a cane to help steady my increasingly wooden gait, and my voice began to take on a certain drawl in more and more tired moments.

In December I returned to the clinic, this time to the doctor. I studied Dr. N as I anxiously shared my bad news: no improvement yet. He had a cold, serious demeanor, seemingly annoyed and stressed before even meeting me, and made it clear he wasn't interested in unnecessary conversation. He tested me again, confirming the nurse's findings, and prescribed me a different slew of drugs and potions in the hope they would finally penetrate the sophisticated defenses of Lyme and coinfections in a noticeable way. Yet this doctor I had waited so many months to meet gave me scant confidence. Every month into the new year I'd return, saying, "I'm getting worse," and every month he seemed progressively more hostile with me and my resistant infection. He'd up the ante with stronger medicine but offer few words of encouragement.

In between these ever-discouraging appointments, I adapted to my new reality and its ever-progressive symptoms as best I could. There was a certain rhythm to it. After my left hand, wrist, and arm, it was my right hand, wrist, and arm. I became slower at pulling on a sweater, eating a taco, washing my face. My arms became heavier, making gesturing or hugging or waving less worth the effort. When I began bumping my hips into furniture due to poor balance, I learned to move slower. Each step eventually became measured, lest I lose my balance and have a fall. Meanwhile, I reminded myself no one ever died of embarrassment.

My new unspoken mantra became adapt, breathe, adapt more, breathe. Can't get ahold of my waistband to pull my pants down? Use the pockets, tugging an inch on the right then an inch on the left, always with one hand on something steadying my balance. Switch hands, repeat. Switch, repeat. Adjust my feet ever so slightly. Lower myself onto the toilet slowly enough that the ricochet effect doesn't knock me against the tank and make my teeth rattle.

The daylight of my own future faded a little each week as I slid further into the underworld of illness. All of my panicked attempts at climbing back to the living, where my family and friends were all yelling encouragements to me, only seemed to result in slipping farther into the darkness of the unknown. I was alone, it was cold, and I had had enough of this grand drama. And yet story after story of people debilitated by Lyme, who finally found a strong enough protocol and recovered the use of their limbs or voice or mind, strengthened the nailhold I still had. *I will be one of those people. I have to be. I will find the route back to the surface, and oh, how sweet that earth will taste.*

6.
Being Ghosted, Being Held

WINTER 2016

I f attachment theory is correct, that we humans have four basic
types of relational patterns—secure, anxious, avoidant, or disorganized—then it stands to reason that stress added into the mix
can easily intensify our grooves. And disabling and life-altering
disease is stressful for all involved, whether patient, friend, or family. Soon after diagnosis I'd start to hear stories about people with
ALS or other devastating diseases flat out left by their spouses or
immediate family, who essentially say, "I didn't sign up for this."
Once done shivering at the idea, I wondered what they thought
they were signing up for by daring to love another mortal.

If anyone had an excuse to jump ship because their mate got
sick, I figured it was John. I was diagnosed ten months into our

marriage, after which my various treatment attempts and appointments would become increasingly expensive and time-consuming for both of us. We would still hike, go on dates, and socialize—we even went camping once with friends, which is hard without all hands on deck—but the quality of these activities shifted as an unknown future hung threatening in the air. Being that John was a decade and a half older than me, and I had made peace upon marriage that I would likely be caring for my beloved in his geriatric years, my thirty-something-going-on-debilitated was a twist neither of us had anticipated.

In February, after it was clear the oral antibiotics weren't producing results, I agreed to let John give me injections of Bicillin, a newer cousin to penicillin. Always willing to help out in whatever way my treatment efforts required, we quickly realized this one would take a lot from him. Perhaps it was due to the doctor barely taking the time to tell him where exactly to stick the needle to reach the right muscle, or perhaps it was my ability to melt in the face (or in this case, the butt) of big needles. All I know is that each time I lay face down on our guest bed, John moving as gently and carefully as possible to ready the needle, soon after he began to inject the medicine I was met with a sear of sharp, piercing pain so strong that I screeched once before promptly bursting into tears. It hurt—*bad.* It didn't help that each injection took half an hour, since the thickly viscous medicine just didn't want to push out. Blood got involved somehow. John tried to soothe me through his own sympathetic tears by providing regular progress updates: "We're a quarter done, babe. I know it hurts. Just try to relax. You gotta relax a little." We were both drenched in sweat from the stress.

We did this routine about nine times before I admitted I had only progressed to a new level of lousy thanks to this treatment.

But even though my husband might have felt he got a bum deal of a wife, he never hinted toward it, nor toward bolting. Instead, over the coming months I'd watch him lean in closer, challenging himself to be an adult and loyally serve and honor me like he'd vowed to do on that hot July day with our family and friends sitting in sacred witness. It was as if we teamed up to confront the common adversary and threat of my illness, learning in the process that going through medical hell with someone can be strangely bonding.

Meanwhile, colleagues were showing up with flowers, food, and resources. Ex-boyfriends reached out with encouragement. People in our sangha donated generously. Our immediate families started flying out to help us with tasks that began piling up. While the attention was helpful in practical ways, often the most important message was just "We see you. We give a damn. And we know it's important to let you know."

Most close friends got even closer. They visited weekly and let me explore my hopes and fears over lunch or tea. If they didn't pretend my existential cliff wasn't real, or explain how theirs was bigger; if they could handle my tenuous grip without collapsing from their own panic; if they approached with a spacious humility which didn't exclude humor, with time, I would accept their reach for me. They let me pour my grieving body into their arms, my hot tears inevitably dousing whatever shirt they had on, sometimes joining my cries, sharing their own dismay without reservation. Learning I could take time to pull myself back from the most immediate ledge without apologizing for big feelings was an unexpected gift.

As my disability progressed, they'd offer more personalized attention: one would wash and henna my hair over the sink, and take the tweezers I could no longer grasp to my wild eyebrows; one would massage my hands, trying to straighten out my increasingly curled, atrophied fingers; one would bring *Vogue* magazine and help me binge-watch early seasons of *Sex and the City*. During these visits, some toyed with their teabags, clearly hesitating to tell me what difficulties they were going through out of fear that it would burden or insult me somehow, as if I'd snort, "You call *that* a problem?" before rightly catching myself. *Give my self-restraint some credit, people! I'm still a Libra, for Chrissakes.* Instead I reminded them I wasn't fragile, *and besides,* I needed to be reminded I wasn't alone in my existential dismay. So most of them proceeded to share generously. Underneath the appearance of happy, functional lives lurked fears of divorce, addiction, self-abuse, mental illness in the family, financial worries, health threats, depression, loss of direction, loss of meaning. Mostly, I could meet them in their complex, messy experiences in a fuller way than I could when my life was more-or-less adhering to my own peachy plans. Pretense disappeared. *Pain school.*

———

Though most of my relationships deepened despite my illness, some floundered in anxiety or avoidance as a result. The contrast was sharp. As I twirled further into an unpredictable future, some people did not only *not* lean in but wholly checked out, sometimes without a word or a wave. And I was routinely shocked by who did this, even more than how they did it, as I could never have predicted who would make that list ahead of time.

Take the director of the DUI treatment agency where I had done some contract work for a few years before my diagnosis. Cantankerous overall but fatherly and affable with me, he had always offered me as much work as I wanted, even telling newer colleagues I was "the one to watch," "the best," his "favorite." A month or so after my ALS diagnosis, once the promising results about Lyme were rolling in, we sat in his office for a sweet, supportive-seeming face-to-face conversation, wherein he championed me in my life and ongoing work. He didn't ask about how long I wanted to continue working if my disability progressed; nor did he share any concerns about the quality of my work changing due to stress. I exited the meeting grateful to have such a humane, communicative boss. Yet the next day, *surprise!* He had his office manager email me to say I was to terminate with all my clients by the end of the week so I could "rest," forgoing any further direct contact with me.

Or there was the close friend who had enjoyed my support and encouragement during our weekly outings for two years before my diagnosis; who had reveled in the mild debauchery at my bachelorette party, and assisted at our wedding on my handpicked bridal brigade; who nonetheless all but stopped calling, texting, or emailing once I was diagnosed; who never responded to my desperate message months later, "Um, where the hell'd you go?"

Even if not a close friendship, I couldn't dismiss the impact of my hairstylist who had reliably chatted me up during each seasonal visit we'd had for years; who would no longer bother to even offer small talk once my illness started showing enough to alter my voice and mobility in her studio, even after I explained why; who perhaps thought neurological malfunction was contagious and a disapproving silence would protect her.

Soon after the ALS diagnosis I had sent some very straightforward emails and messages directly to some old friends and family, all of whom I had once been close with, and who I suspected hadn't yet heard the news. Despite getting read receipts, a surprising number failed to respond at all. A few eventually responded as if I hadn't mentioned a terminal prognosis, instead asking how my new marriage was going or if I liked the weather in Colorado. One even signed off with the strangely dissociative, "I hope things are great!"

After each such encounter—or *non*-encounter—I felt that rebounding *dooiiing!* effect that happens when an anvil drops on Wile E. Coyote. Only, the stunned feeling didn't simply evaporate, it hung around in my heart, leaving me to wonder what makes good people turn tail so unapologetically in the face of another's misfortune. Many of them, I'd learn later, had talked of my diagnosis with others, sometimes clucking at the horror of it—yet never bothering to reply to my messages. I realized this meant they were more comfortable with the likelihood of my dying without saying a word than taking the time to reach out and say, however awkwardly, "I hear that. I care. I'm sorry."

Ouch.

But despite how personal it all felt, I was simply being schooled in a reality I'd been privileged to ignore until now: people don't like thinking of death, or vulnerability, perhaps even more so in a peer. It takes courage to behold impermanence so honestly, let alone talk about it. It's easier to keep the nagging discomfort of the transience of life at a tolerable distance, even if it means failing to show up for someone at a time that they could use a little acknowledgement and contact. But as much as us Americans want to act rugged and independent and unfazed by difficulty, a basic truth remains: we are social beings who crave meaningful connection and support from our tribes, and this is even more true when things start falling apart.

Adding to the complications is how debilitating illness has a tendency to disgust people, especially when they can't empathize. All too many of us living with disease or disability learn sobering lessons about others' patience and understanding the hard way, when we most need our social networks to pull through. Perhaps even more so for those with invisible disabilities—like my chronic fatigue before ALS—friends and family may become less helpful or interested, refusing to "feed cries for attention," perhaps indulging in harsh judgment or New Age-style superiority about just needing to "raise one's vibration." And some doctors even do the same thing when they don't understand someone's symptoms, forgoing curiosity or due diligence, implying the symptoms arise solely from mental or emotional weakness; an institutionalized gaslighting. *Cough, Infectious Diseases Society of America.*

———

But being abandoned by individual people is one thing; feeling abandoned by the most elemental relationship one could have, with destiny, the universe, Source itself is quite another. Like most people will, I carried over the attachment style adopted toward my parents in childhood—largely avoidant, with anxious tinges—to my relationship to and conception of the divine. But though I had long shed any traditional notion of God, and was working toward a secure attachment with life itself in adulthood, I had reserved just enough Judeo-Christian obedience to follow a formula designed to please any cosmic decision-makers from any conceivable tradition: seek to grow in kindness and morality; pray when necessary; vote for justice; drive a hybrid; appreciate John Prine. Nonetheless I felt as if I'd been carelessly dropped, but without the, "Oops! Big mistake—sorry! Be right there!" shouted down to reassure me and repair the breach.

Whether or not divinely meaningful, my new reality hurt. More than just the big picture of the disability and its life-threatening implications, there were also the countless humiliating details that were increasingly becoming a part of my daily life. Take just my falls from my tipsy gait, many of which were still to come: smashing my face into the bedroom wall, alone, looking for the following week like I had been in a bloody fistfight; or having to lie immobilized on our hallway floor for an hour, alone, waiting for John to walk in and discover me; or the backward one, alone, inside the chicken coop which was overdue for a cleaning; or the sideways one, alone, into a river of giant biting black ants who would immediately carve their creepy path up my yoga pants.

Or there was the figurative sense of aloneness, exacerbated when entering an exercise class for adults with Parkinson's and MS, only to find I was the least capable participant, everyone else was twice my age, and the blasted pop music still wasn't loud enough to drown out my weeping during the seated arm circles. There were the growing instances where strangers assumed my drawl or clumsiness were due to intoxication and became cruelly judgmental as a result. It's the small insults that have a way of adding up over time.

So I hissed at whatever unknowable forces were responsible for my predicament, *Watch it. I have a certain pluck to rise on trembling legs and brush myself off for another round with chance, but certain blows are hard for even the most determined and faithful among us to rise from. Is that what you want, you, you—whatever the fuck tormentor you are? To break me?* Debilitating illness is the breeding ground for a cosmic-level attachment disorder.

But just when I wanted to collapse into cynicism, start smoking cigarettes, and finally commit to Nietzsche via audiobook—just when I was ready to give up for good on the idea of any sacred witness to my inherent dignity, that is—I'd get a big, fat kiss on the lips by a wildly creative turn of events. Like Anu showing up upon asking. Like the check arriving after a prayer for money, in the amount I specified. There were everyday examples too: a bubbly friend would show up with a baked chicken, ready to gossip in the perfect moment; someone would come along and tend my bruises, cooing just enough in a gentle tone; other exercise-class participants, themselves disabled but determined, would kindly cheer me on through my tears. And just when I began slipping into despair for the hundredth time, an old folk song or new story would catch my ear with a message reminding me of a greater purpose behind challenge.

So I learned to train my attention toward these graces to avoid drowning in patterned negativity or doubt. I practiced affirming that despite those people who failed to show up, there were dozens who *were* showing up, offering endless varieties of care and attention, many of whom I was yet to meet; that the ratio of human support to human rejection was undoubtedly in my favor.

Of course questions remained: How much does chance, circumstance, and privilege shape our views of how generous or withholding life ultimately is? Why do some prayers/visions/intentions seem to get immediate fulfillment, while others never do? Do we always have enough perspective to make solid conclusions about the meaning of events?

Because thank goodness we don't *always* get what we want; thank goodness the world isn't some giant vending machine always doling out the exact treat we desire in the moment. A few months before I met John, I got rudely dumped by that cuteish-but-emotionally-unavailable-Scorpio-with-the-cool-vintage-car. At the time it felt disastrous; in retrospect I feel grateful I endured my post-breakup howling hysterics to emerge again into singledom. Despite my desperate pleas, the universe—or perhaps just the Scorpio—was dead set against honoring my prayers for him to want me, and he never called back. And I just so happened to end up with a love affair a thousand times better than he ever could have offered. Perhaps one marker of maturity is collecting gratitude some prayers never get answered and allowing that recognition to chill us out a bit overall.

Due in part to these continued reminders and in part to the unexplainable marvel known as faith, something within me knew I was never wholly abandoned, even if I tried to insist otherwise. Reality continually presented more nuance, and I couldn't deny that something wise and responsive seemed to be flirting with me, presenting just enough small mercies to encourage me to keep getting out of bed to face the day. That life may hurt, it may seem to make no sense, but there was a bigger container to my suffering—one which also held surprising blessings.

And in some moments I even remembered the most trans-formative prayers are not so much those where we're asking for divine intervention so that circumstances line up in the way we most prefer, but those designed as sacred affirmations to ourselves: that we may find a kind of unwavering workability through trusting life on life's terms, knowing full well that peace can only be found following acceptance of what already is. And since I knew such prayers were always available and only depended on my willing-ness to affirm them, I suspected I could keep cultivating a secure attachment with the big and colorful—and, so often, mercifully kind—palette of life itself.

7.
Exploring the
Roots of Illness

APRIL 2017

As spring warmed up, and because I had not had violent bacterial die-off reactions to the oral antibiotics, I finally earned the long-awaited right to an IV antibiotic drip at home via a PICC line in my arm. In the world of Lyme, this was the big guns, rumored to offer the most hope for penetrating my central nervous system. Day after day I prayed as the magical elixir seeped into my veins at our kitchen table, cooing to the medicine, telling it where to go and what to do, hopeful that I'd slowly start growing stronger as the infection was beaten back.

About a week into starting the IV therapy, I felt strong enough to walk my new rolling walker a hundred yards down our street before turning around. *Triumph!* I plodded home with excited tears, flopping into my cushy living-room chair to call Mom and announce, "I think it's working! I feel stronger today!"

She cheered, "Wahoo!"

But the very next day, when my legs felt heavier than they ever had and I couldn't imagine even walking to our mailbox, doubt crept back in.

Three weeks later, back in Dr. N's office and feeling ever weaker, he expressed his own doubt. "If the IV Rocephin was going to work, you would know it by now," he said with a sigh, lining up yet another oral antibiotic cocktail to try. Before the appointment ended, he turned to his assistant with a sick sideways grin to ask rhetorically, "What, is it like ten percent of Lyme-induced ALS patients who *actually* recover any function? Fifteen?" She looked slightly afraid, and shrugged.

I got the message loud and clear: my failure was likely and wouldn't be his fault. *Thanks for the support, Doc.* While bitterly staggering down the clinic hall, I asked myself if I wanted this asshole to get any credit for partnering with me in my impending comeback story.

———

After exhausting the best resources that Colorado seemed able to offer my failing body, I felt at a crossroads. The losses were mounting: loss of function, loss of money, loss of options, loss of hope. Clearly, quality treatment was not cheap, easy, or available locally—and definitely was not covered by insurance. As much as my working-class roots scoffed at the idea of dropping thousands out of pocket for extended care at some faraway specialized treatment center, this was beginning to look more and more like the only last-ditch option powerful enough to reverse my body's quickly failing course.

Still listening for signs and cues for what to do next, I kept fielding referrals from the Lyme community for the Hansa Center in nearby Kansas, which specialized in treating chronic illness caused by infection. Their website featured video lectures and articles from staff doctors which all argued that while attacking the infection itself was important, the systemic terrain—including the immune system—also needs to be treated. Otherwise, the body doesn't have the necessary oomph to beat back the infection. They highlighted testing methods and intensive treatment which locates and corrects imbalances in organs, hormones, the nervous system, and so on. The more I researched it, the more intrigued I became. Apparently, that's the thing about desperation—even the longshot tickets seem to take on a certain romantic glow.

John liked the idea. My dad and brother agreed something more was in order. Mom even said she could get time off teaching to join me while I was in treatment. It turned out the most resistance I faced came from myself. In my mind, I repeatedly turned over the same question:

Aren't big chunks of money to be used only for unavoidable necessities, like going back to school, or replacing the refrigerator, or a ten-year anniversary trip to tour crop circles in England?

Then I remembered that without a body none of that would be necessary, and not having a wife would make it all less fun for John.

After about a dozen such enlightening inquiries during hours meant for sleep—and absent anyone willing to sit me down and temper my frantic, confused decision-making—I committed to trying the expensive plunge. And to our surprise, an online fund-raiser raised the necessary 10K to cover the trip within only days. As the money poured in, my concerns about going into debt over it became irrelevant. *So watch out Kansas, here we come.*

———

When my mother arrived to meet us at our apartment rental in Wichita a few weeks later, all chatty smiles, I had that familiar wave of giddy playfulness and adolescent guardedness she managed to pull from me well into adulthood.

"Hello, my darling daughter," she said, offering a hug as John stumbled inside with a few of her seven heavy bags. After silently noting my new stagger and remarking how perfect our Airbnb was, she helped John move her luggage into her little bedroom to promptly begin unpacking.

True to form, we would soon get to hear the detailed narrative of her thoughts behind every item she pulled from her cache. "Sandals, in case it's warm and we have time for a walk. They aren't as great as Crocs, but they were eighty percent off clearance at Kohls. I got them in blue too, see? Wrapping paper, in case there's someone to leave a gift for—you never know! Garden gloves, in case there's some weeding to do. I left out the hand shovel last minute. What—why are you looking at me like that? Did I bring too much? Do you think this is *funny*?" she asked, laughing.

While nodding, I noted she'd brought enough random snacks to feed the entire Center for a week, reminding her the stores in Kansas probably had food. With a grin and a shrug, she replied,

"I like to be prepared. It's a personal problem." John had by this time mysteriously disappeared.

In the midst of this colorful unpacking saga, I tried to remind myself how fortunate I was that she was willing and able to join me for the two-week stay so John could return to Colorado to work. All wackiness aside, she was still doing the Mom-job happily and with flourish, so I suspected I should only feel grateful. And, with that, another *effing* opportunity in personal growth had officially arrived.

—

The next morning, we had to show up at the Hansa Center at nine to start our orientation. By this point I had lost so much balance that I could only teeter along unsteadily without my walker, the tool I had too much pride to use in public unless absolutely necessary. While exhibiting a well-trained courtesy, a receptionist gave us a tour of the two-story building, patient with me as I hobbled along slowly, Mom and John just behind. She pointed out various treatment rooms I would be spending time in, where we could store our things and get lunch, and introduced us to other staff along the way. My mother asked the receptionist questions to which I already knew the answers, sparking my impatience, but I reminded myself we had a long two weeks ahead together and it'd be wise to distribute my complaints against her evenly.

After a begrudging goodbye with John before he caught a ride to the airport, I was scheduled to begin the in-house testing. Beyond the functional medicine approach to evaluating blood-work, the testing was, well, *unconventional*. At first, I didn't mind. I had read convincing reviews on unaffiliated Lyme discussion forums from self-described impossible cases who had significant turnarounds here after nothing else worked, leaving me hopeful that their approach might address a big blind spot my past efforts had missed. But even though I had read about the "computerized regulation thermography," when I realized it required an unfortunate amount of nakedness as a strange gun-like reader was held to various points of my shivering body by a teenaged attendant, I heard my practical doubts kick in. *Is this a grand, cuckoo racket? Where am I? God, I hope this expense is worth it.*

The next step was to meet with the doctor who was assigned to me. Waiting for Dr. C to retrieve me from the lobby for the first time left me queasy, as I was now familiar with the subtle variations in doctors' egos and outlooks which could make or break a useful relationship. Plus, Mom wanted to join me for the meeting—a meeting wherein I'd be expected to confess every sundry detail of my well-being, or lack thereof—which made me want to hyperventilate a little. I tried to be diplomatic in telling her I wanted to do this first one alone. "Oh... okay," she replied in a small voice, looking like she might cry. Guilt threatened to set in, but I gave it a stern talking-to: *Teri, I am trying to save my life, and if I feel more comfortable seeing the doctor alone, so be it. I no longer have the luxury to put others' needs first;* such a sensible, non-convincing argument.

Within minutes Dr. C emerged from the hallway to introduce himself. With a spacious warmth he led me back to his office, inviting me to settle in. We got to work discussing my symptoms, medical history, and test results, and his note taking allowed me to look around at his shelves filled with thousands of supplements and remedies. When asked about my goals for treatment, I laid out a modest plan for at least slowing my symptoms, instead of confessing my true wish: "Uh, save my life and return me to normal? Preferably by the end of the week."

In addition to exploring markers of physical health, he gently asked about my mental and emotional health, and I suddenly realized I already had a doctor-crush. *Gawsh*...

"Well, I've done a ton of emotional work, and have overcome a lot of dissociative patterns and developmental trauma... am still learning self-care and forgiveness... kind of average stuff you might expect coming out a well-meaning, addictive family system."

He nodded.

"But, if I'm honest, I'm still compulsively busy and ambitiously wound up to a stressful degree. Oh, and I feel what everyone else is feeling before they know they're feeling it, and... that's hard... and annoying... uh... like with my mother. You'll meet her tomorrow."

He chuckled knowingly, clearly getting the code.

Inviting me to hop on his treatment table, he then began doing a kind of "bioresonance" testing—a far-out cousin to muscle testing—to find the order of issues that needed to be addressed within me. This all made enough sense; by this time I knew that the phrase "Lyme disease" is often used as shorthand to refer to a complex, multisystemic illness which can include immune dysfunction, genetic factors, toxin and viral load, nutritional deficiencies, parasitic infections, fungal overgrowth, metabolic dysfunction and coinfections. As such, it is rarely an easy or simple fix, and needs to be addressed by finding the right treatment for the right layer in the right order.

Attempting to not overwhelm me all at once, Dr. C loaded me up with about seven new protocols for day one, knowing I would be back daily for the next two weeks for further testing and tweaking, and assigned me a treatment schedule. By this point I decided he was what I most wanted in a physician: caring, intelligent, respectful, present, and, most importantly to me at this time, willing to believe that radical healing is possible.

At the end of our meeting, I asked him, "So do you think there's still any hope for me?"

He chuckled, "Hope? Well, you're still here, aren't ya?"

———

Throughout my stay, I carefully observed the other patients' reports of symptoms, diagnoses, and signs of recovery. It didn't take long to decide that I was in the most dire situation out of everyone at the center, a special designation I wasn't proud of winning. I quickly became accustomed to fielding encouragements from other patients in the halls or break area: "You're walking stronger today!"; "I know you're healing!"; "You got this!" I felt like a mascot, the one who others were secretly relieved to be in better shape than. *Why couldn't I just have chronic fatigue? MS? Fibromyalgia? Those would surely be an emotional cakewalk in comparison.* I even envied the nice Scottish woman with great hair and stage-two stomach cancer, who could walk and talk just fine.

So near the end of treatment week one when a young person clearly more ill than I rolled in in a reclining wheelchair resembling a stretcher, I felt relief that I wasn't the most extreme long-shot patient willing to take a risk on this unconventional treatment method. This teenager, who had reportedly been excelling at sports a year earlier, was now on oxygen, voiceless, and completely dependent upon his parents to address his basic needs. His legs were pencils from muscle atrophy. The fact that his illness had spiraled fiercely in the months after a tick bite only served to remind me of how powerful a stealth bacterial infection can be and renewed my determination to fight this wicked illness—both for my own sake and for everyone else who stands to be debilitated by one.

Over tea in the lounge between treatments, patients and their families would share tables and discuss their dismay that the FDA and CDC could get away with repeatedly ignoring chronic Lyme, thereby allowing this public health crisis to go unnoticed. Stories slipped out one after another about strings of clueless doctors, outrageous bills, being dropped by insurers, and missed windows for early intervention. Less discussed were the corporations being allowed to put toxins in our food, water, air and buildings, pre-disposing us all to greater levels of illness; yet these realities were implied in the conversations about needing organic food and filtered water, comparing detox methods and air purifiers. I noted how in the absence of quality state-sponsored public health measures, families are left to themselves to shore the gaps. And I knew these gaps are much bigger for some than for others.

We women, mostly white and middle class, would sit draped with plush towels in the sauna, sighing and clucking about how it wasn't right that so many people were hurting from poorly under-stood chronic illnesses with little options for help. Even though most of us had been able to come only through fundraisers or significant personal financial risk, it seemed we knew we were the lucky ones, having the privilege of access to personalized treatment that many people couldn't afford or might not even know existed. We had the resources to choose more expensive food, to largely choose where we live and work, and to afford these seemingly non-stop remedies and treatments in the hope they provide some useful benefit.

My thoughts went further, to how I never had to question if a doctor's dismissal of me was due to my race or gender expression or education level or first language. Sitting there both grateful and guilty that I was fortunate enough to get the opportunity to undo the reality of my failing body, I began to suspect the roots of chronic illness, and the likelihood of finding adequate treatment for it, were both more complex and more heartbreaking than even I had imagined.

Meanwhile, a looming question remained: Why do some of us get drastically sicker than others, even with similar histories? Despite the Lyme test results, I had no obvious answers to why I could end up so sick. Very few of all those infected with Lyme also end up with ALS, so why had my infection—if it was indeed the deciding factor which spiraled my health—become so severe? Was I set up for it by the daily Pop Tarts that carried me through junior high, or the homemade soda can pipes I used to smoke weed from as a high-school sophomore? The summers spent working as a wilderness guide with troubled teens, cooking beans in thin "billycan" aluminum over open fires? Or maybe the series of vaccines required to travel to Asia, or the half-dozen afternoons swimming in the murky Boulder reservoir? Sometimes, I'd be grasping so much for answers that I thought I'd eaten too much non-organic almond butter or spent too much time on my cell phone, irradiating my brain. It didn't matter to me that these were all average risks my generation of peers had more or less taken; I still questioned why I hadn't somehow headed off this level of physiological failure before it had become a terrible crisis.

But this line of reflective obsession was far from new. By this point I'd already spent much of the past year cataloging what I increasingly understood as chronic symptoms before the ALS. The more I thought, the more I found.

I remembered how, once I hit thirty, after taking a challenging position counseling inmates at the county jail and moving into a hundred-year-old communal house, new symptoms came on fast and hard. Over the following months I started having joint stiffness, chronic hives, serious fatigue, and brain fog. My desire for exercise dwindled to walking about a mile or, on good days, slowly riding my bike around town—extremely uncharacteristic for my usually active self. Sometimes I'd have to fight to keep my eyes open in sessions with clients, when all I really wanted to do was go home and crawl into bed.

After mold was discovered in the communal house, I moved in with John and quit working at the jail so I could focus on private practice. And within weeks of these two changes, my overwhelming fatigue and brain fog began to spontaneously subside, and I regained the energy to exercise. It seemed like I had found and eliminated the culprit. But strangely, my newfound strengths were quickly offset by other new symptoms: skin redness, ear ringing, sound sensitivity, bug-crawling sensations, tingly hands upon waking, burning heels at night, random muscle twitches. My eyes and face took on a yellow hue of jaundice, despite eating healthier than ever. Clearly, something was wrong.

Internet research had me spinning with confusion about my symptoms, and the acupuncturist and naturopath I visited were stumped. Allopathic doctors were no better, took me less seriously, and had harsher lighting to boot. A very disinterested dermatologist spent the five minutes required to diagnose me with something called dermographism and prescribe an antihistamine, saying I had no bugs on my body. After humiliating me for wanting answers to the cause of my symptoms, she left the exam room, leaving her embarrassed attendant to awkwardly hand me tissues as I cried. I walked out even more convinced conventional medicine had nothing to offer me.

All these symptoms together hinted at a troubling level of systemic imbalance causing immune and neurological dysfunction. But I didn't know the extent of the threat; I was just trying to live my busy, full life. And so my health remained under-addressed, until finally in the fall of 2015 my left-arm weakness caught my attention.

———

The long days at the center, stumbling between treatment rooms, getting oxygen up my nose and massages to my sluggish lymph, sitting in fancy magnetic chairs which were doing fancy electric things to my cells, gave me a lot of time to consider all of this. I thought of the conundrum in general which people with chronic mystery symptoms face: first, they're seen as overreacting and their symptoms are all in their head; next, they've waited too long and have been diagnosed with something deemed incurable, and perhaps deadly. Then, figuring out the right treatment—and, most often, its costs—is on the patient.

Though at this point we had spent around $20–30K, I knew it wasn't uncommon for those with chronic illness to spend hundreds of thousands of dollars to get care, sometimes selling their homes to afford treatment. And the community they come from, their race, their support system, their education level, and a host of other factors outside of their control play a large role in determining what type of healthcare, if any, they have access to and ultimately receive. So though I was one of the sickest in the center and unlucky because of it, I could also see ways in which I was extraordinarily fortunate to even be there, funded by my community, with my husband's support and my mother by my side. If anyone with my illness had a shot at recovery on an access-to-treatment basis, I figured I was a top contender. This recognition allowed me to turn my sights toward the one factor of nervous-system healing I had yet to sufficiently master: my unruly mind.

8.
Mind/Body
Blame and Shame

erhaps there is no situation more perfect to show any grown adult their lingering emotional hang-ups than two weeks in constant proximity with their mother. Toss in a growing physical dependence on her help, the looming threat of your own mortality, a maddening amount of shared decision-making, and things suddenly get real. Meaning, the gloves of restraint are too readily coming off. Or at least that's how it worked for me.

By the end of each day of treatment I was emotionally and physically spent, ready to just eat a quiet dinner, video call John, and get to sleep early. But first I had to navigate a steady stream of inquiries from Mom, each of which included heavy looks in my direction and expectations of complete answers: "Do we turn right or left here? Should we take the expressway? Is this the turn? Oh no, did I miss it? Are you tired? What do you need help with tonight? What do you want for dinner? What kind of cooking oil should I use with that? Should we stop at the store?" And my favorite, "Am I bothering you?"

And so it was: amidst the big questions of life and death sat an ongoing parade of small interactions which meant nothing and yet somehow everything: The questions of where I went "wrong" in life to end up here, and what could still change my destiny for the better... Of what relationship patterns I needed to do differently in order to heal, or to *not* physically heal but at least die with the satisfaction of knowing I'd grown as much as possible in being able to honor the people I care about without betraying myself in the process... Of how many conversations should be used to grow, versus practicing relaxation, surrender, and enjoying the moment with imperfect company. In other words, some of the most foundational tensions to life itself.

But in the immediate moment, of course, her questions were all valid and innocent enough; she wanted to help, even if doing so required me to reassure or direct her with energy I didn't have to spare. *Wait*, I thought. *Aren't I the sick one needing help? Why do I have to work so hard still? Couldn't you take some of the burden of attention off me for once, inhabit your own damn body, and just figure stuff out?*

I didn't say these types of things half as much as I thought them. Her *wanting* to help only added a layer of guilt on top of the irritation, therefore I decided we were simply enacting the dirty deal that many parents unconsciously present their children: *I'm going to martyr myself to meet your needs, and you'll play along with unquestioning devotion. If you don't, I'll become the victim of your ingratitude and will take opportunities to lay overt or subtle guilt trips on you, which will ultimately be so powerful that before long you'll become an expert on laying them on yourself.* To which the child could reply, *Wait, I don't remember signing up for that.* And so begins the parent/child messiness which replicates itself through generations and guarantees to keep bars and therapists in business for a long time.

So while grocery shopping for dinner on the way to our Airbnb, we continued to swim in the murky, codependent waters of my youth—familiar territory, but this time with the added pressure of neurodegenerative disease in the mix. We tried to work it out while standing in the rice-cracker aisle, which went something like this:

Mom: "Explain again why my smiling is so annoying to you?"

Me: "Because it's constant. Is it real? I wonder, *Where* are *you?* Must we pretend this shit sandwich is just a feast of joy? If you can't acknowledge your anxiety in a situation this scary, how am I supposed to open up with my messy feelings? Plus, why can't you just use your GPS like everyone else?"

Mom: "Oh! Well." She put on a tight grin and continued under her breath, "Sorry. I know. I'm just a piece of shit. Sorry you have to deal with me."

Me, with exaggerated teenage eyeroll: "Mom, that's it! Don't do that!"

Mom, with exaggerated sighing: "It's just that you always have a better sense of direction and I'm so ditzy. Ms. Ditzy."

Me: "But I get tired of always being the one with the answers. I can't be your 'rock' right now! I just want to be your daughter for now, you know?"

Mom: "But... everything comes so naturally to you. I'm just not as... *together* as you are, and I want to do it right. I smile because I'm happy to be with you. Is that so wrong? To be happy?" She looked genuinely perplexed.

I'd sigh and clumsily stomp away with the grocery cart in search of chard, filing through my memories for undeniable examples of confusing, not-ideal parenting to remind myself I wasn't nuts. Eventually, having thoroughly justified my anger to myself in the produce aisle, she'd turn the corner, flash a big smile, and say, "Hi! Ready to check out?"

Tired of the conflict, feeling guilt for being angry at someone unable to understand my frustration, I'd say yes, averting eye contact.

And so it went.

———

Even though my ire had new fuel in the context of post-diagnosis relating, the pattern of role confusion between my mother and I had a long history, as did her difficulty acknowledging the anxiety driving her neediness and insecurity. Or at least this was one of my armchair assessments, courtesy of the risk she took in birthing a child who would someday study psychology: nonconsensual diagnosis.

The hidden specter behind much of this ongoing conflict with her was her partner in crime, my father. Ah, Dad. Like so many other "empaths" who develop abilities to read other's emotions at a supernatural rate, my brother and I began training young. As an ex-Marine discharged due to injury and thus narrowly escaping Vietnam, Dad made it clear that the only big feelings that would be tolerated in our family would be his own. As a toddler I learned I should hold myself together, lest someone much bigger decide to show me what a tantrum *really* looked like.

But it's not that Dad was an across-the-board tyrant; few parents are. Full of contradiction, he was a cruel bully when I wanted to quit after ten years of fastpitch softball competition but a remarkably patient coach otherwise; vicious whenever anyone suggested he shouldn't drink and drive us around but often fun and playful two or three drinks in; would wax philosophic in his idealization of nature yet would pose for photos with an unabashed grin when holding the limp head of a deer in one hand, rifle in the other, blood still everywhere. But despite the good moments and qualities, his mood twists in the car or at home occurred unpredictably enough, after which all blame was usually turned on whomever was nearest or most convenient. Which left the rest of us in a familiar state of terrified tiptoe.

This is where Mom comes in—or perhaps more importantly, *didn't* come in. Unwilling or unable to safely set limits on his disorderly law and order approach, Mom modeled that the best thing we could do is to let him get away with whatever theatrics he chose, perhaps pouring him a drink in the process. She'd say to him and to us in a pleading tone, "We're just going to be okay. We're fine, it's fine," always in response to clearly *not*-fine things—in case the rest of us got confused by what we were seeing and feeling. And thus, my rage at Dad's behavior got mixed up with bewilderment about how Mom shrank in the face of it—or even enabled it.

My professional training suggested this sort of "everything's fine"-type dissociation is simply a well-fortified defense, not terribly uncommon in a culture where bland optimism is seen as the only valid response to nearly any challenge—or, for that matter, in a relationship which rightly feels dangerous. Either way, a parent's enduring denial of the existence of threatening realities can be especially harmful to children, who are rapidly developing their understanding of the world, relationships, and trust in their own perceptions. One family therapy theory goes like this: Whenever anyone refuses to acknowledge their own difficult feelings and insists on blanketing complex realities with undiscriminating positivity, usually someone *else* within the family system or relationship is unconsciously being asked to "hold" those feelings. This unspoken deal tends to anger or hurt anyone sensitive to emotional manipulation, even if they have no way to name their own feelings, in which case their anger or overwhelm will still find a sideways expression (including, even, through symptoms in their own body).

This is why the "identified patient" (IP) or family member most afflicted with big symptoms, whether physical, emotional, or mental, isn't necessarily the root of the issue. Instead, as the most sensitive or vulnerable in the bunch, the IP is often merely a symptom of some larger dysfunctional current within the family, group, or society. (Kind of similar to the idea that a chronic infection isn't always the root problem so much as the unbalanced or vulnerable microbiome and immune system which makes one more susceptible to being knocked out by common toxins or pathogens we're all more or less exposed to.) Hence my thinking that working to encourage Mom's acknowledgement and owning of her own feelings (and competence) might in a way unburden me. It was a theory, at least, even if arguably mired in good ol' codependent dynamics itself.

But the problem with other people—*dang them*—is they're difficult to control. And really, that's all Mom was ever trying to do by insisting "everything's fine" when it wasn't—keep her own conflicted feelings, and the rest of ours, in check and underground.

If she didn't make her own decisions or acknowledge her own feelings, she couldn't be blamed for being "wrong"—and risk rejection or punishment.

My brother and I developed our own methods for control, of course. Rob, half-brother via Dad and seven years my senior, disappeared into guarded, noncommittal agreeability which, when combined with his charm and sapphire eyes, rendered him the endlessly unreachable enigma of the family; once grown this meant becoming a sheriff's officer with an appointment on the hostage response unit. I disappeared into quiet vigilance, Girl Scout cookies and Nintendo, then pot, then a strange perfectionism, eventually evolving from the "parentified child" who emotionally tends to her caregivers in a role reversal, into the "natural" psychotherapist, well suited to working with wounded or dangerous people (my most common clientele were inmates prone to violence or psychosis, repeat DUI offenders, sex offenders, and drug bosses on federal parole). Both my brother and I ended up with a high tolerance for situational intensity and a higher-than-average ability to read others' emotional temperature and intent (and disarm accordingly); childhood survival strategies which later became marketable skills.

I was long aware that a childhood characterized by midgrade fear, double binds, and significant emotional repression hints toward a flavor of developmental trauma. And by the time I was stomping and steaming my way through the produce aisle of the Wichita health-food store, I couldn't help but think about the groundbreaking findings of the Adverse Childhood Experiences (ACEs) study from the 1990s: the more stresses and traumas one endures in childhood, the more likely one is to develop chronic mental or physical illness in their adulthood. This study influenced the way therapists look at disease and healing as simultaneous physical and psychological processes, and is often interpreted to suggest that the seeds for immune dysfunction may be planted long before one becomes symptomatic.

But as much as blaming my parents for my susceptibility to illness was tempting, I knew as an adult my stress was ultimately my responsibility to address; blaming them would not fly, nor help. The damage from decades ago couldn't be undone. What's more, they didn't want me to end up sick; they were both heartbroken by it. And they had always provided structure, protection, and loving attention to the best of their abilities, both of them improving in notable ways upon the parenting they had received, both of them comfortably inside the bell curve of emotional literacy for their genders and generations. They simply managed with the emotional toolbox handed down to them, with the missing skills and potentials unnoticed and unaccounted for. They were traumatized, complex, imperfect, often lovely, and mostly well-meaning beings who had made repeated mistakes while trying to do their best. And guess what? Join the fucking club. It's big.

Knowing this, and thereby tempering my resentments toward Mom while on this trip, all questions of blame frolicked in a larger playground of blaming myself. Of course I had been exposed to the sloppier realms of New Age thinking, where we always "create" our reality. I'd already waded into the waters of body/mind-heavy German New Medicine where all illness is seen to arrive from internal conflict. I'd briefly followed the work of fundamentalist wellness practitioners who would argue that there is no physical basis for illness outside of what one's own fear or negativity has created; unsurprisingly, these folks were mostly well-off, white, loath to acknowledge systemic, environmental, or genetic realities which could affect health; some even held a predictable fascination with the libertarian politics of Ayn Rand. It would take more time for me to shake myself awake from these ableist, lopsided narratives of responsibility in illness and come to see they reflected yet another fantasy grasp for control over the timeless realities of vulnerability, aging, and death. I wasn't there yet; I wanted the control, even if assuming it came wrapped up in guilt, shame, and utter delusion.

But even this idea of control over and responsibility for one's illness, as blaming and smug as it can be, is not *such* a far leap from the growing theories in medical research that emotional stress plays a large role in many disease processes—theories to which the ACE study is often assumed to give credence. By this point I had already done over a decade of my own trauma therapy, workshops, forgiveness work, meditation retreats, and twelve-step programs. Had it been enough to sufficiently unburden my immune system of chronic, toxic stress? There's always more self-improvement work to do if one goes looking: *What about my art of grudge holding, my ongoing terror of exposing vulnerability to others, my "Sunday anxiety," existential dread when I'm not busy with whatever? Couldn't those be symptoms of something still hurting inside, something that feeds illness?* Assuming responsibility for my predicament meant that somehow, maybe I could still fix it, even if I knew that spinning in analysis and self-blame was not the way.

——

Only a week or two after diagnosis I had received an email invite for coffee from Dr. Bob, one of my long-time mentors in all things psychotherapy. He said he had heard from John about my situation and wanted to offer his support. Because I so loved the guy I happily agreed; as a bike-riding, emotionally literate, Buddhist-informed Jewish liberal from New York, he offered a novel alternative to the father archetype I'd so far known. Since being a graduate student in his courses a decade prior and eventually becoming his teaching assistant and supervisee, he had taught me the value of staying humble as a therapist and how to regard the vocation as an ongoing art form, skill, and labor of love. This meant I knew I was safe to bring my mental and emotional messiness to him, just as I had done many times before with various client quandaries.

As we sat there on the empty back patio of Vic's Coffee one bright weekday afternoon just days later, I shakily croaked out my panicked plan for radical self-healing. Because I thought the mind/body connection is powerful, and harboring resentments depresses immunity, I suspected forgiveness was the biggest metaphysical *thing* that I must reckon with if I wanted a fighting chance. So I explained through tears how I needed to forgive others more for their imperfections, for their hurtful actions, for their maddening eccentricities which made no sense to me. I shared that I feared that despite all the psychological work I had already done, I had somehow triggered the illness through unresolved complaints against who and what had hurt me in the past; that basically, I must be emotionally defunct in a key way, and it was now showing up in my body.

Bob may have known at this point I had already done plenty of forgiveness work through Al-Anon and other twelve-step programs; that I knew how to list my resentments, how to recognize which personal vulnerabilities and needs they threatened, and how to intend for their removal; that writing down and discussing with my sponsors the hurts I carried helped me develop the cognitive map for the colorful terrain of my discontent. He probably did not know my hurts were largely unremarkable, garden-variety resentments; that like most of us with a heartbeat, I didn't like my safety or integrity threatened, whether by girl-slumber-party bullies decades ago, or all the men through the years who had assumed undue license over my body; that the volume and length of my bitterness didn't always match the offense, like when I'd let the careless close call from a random driver ruin my morning bike ride to work. He could have guessed my own therapy was helpful to unearthing the layers of harsh narratives about the world; that, while some resentments evaporated rather instantly through shining a light of awareness in their direction, others disappeared only to mysteriously arise again later, and others were so deeply rooted that the most I could do was gradually lessen their intensity, like removing grains of rice one by one from a huge platter of spiritual paella.

With tears in his own eyes, Bob just listened to all this said and unsaid story, nodding through my concerns, already familiar with my patterns of self-doubt and outsized responsibility. When I finally paused for air, he dropped in a gentle question. "Teri, what if, instead of focusing on forgiving others as much, you start with forgiving yourself?"

I paused, momentarily stunned. *Myself?* Like any well-timed and skillful intervention, this simple query hit me square between the eyes. "Yeah… Probably… Maybe," I mumbled shakily, attempting to open to the idea.

Of course, this reminder for self-compassion was the most basic instruction, a variation of something I had undoubtedly suggested to countless friends and clients before this moment and something many others had already gently suggested to me. Yet because of the new context and the strength of the witnessing Bob provided me, it struck me as if it was the first time I've ever heard the idea. *Forgive myself...? Really?*

———

Easter weekend followed the first week of treatment. On Saturday morning, Mom packed my rolling walker into the trunk and drove us to the Wichita Botanical Gardens where tulips of every variety greeted us with their proud celebrations of spring. I ambled along with my stiff, tipsy gait, trying to squeeze a little joy out of witnessing the children gallop by. I attempted to smile when sitting on my walker in front of exhibitions, Mom holding up her phone for a picture.

After an hour of watching families of every variety wander past, their lives appearing so terrifically un-tragic, I lost my ability to pretend. Sitting on a rock ledge under a sprawling tree, I began crying more obviously than I ever wished to in public. Mom just sat with me, giving me a light touch on the shoulder.

After a few moments I pulled myself together to ask. "Mom...? Why is this happening to me?"

With tears streaming down her own face, she replied in a shaky voice, "I don't know, honey. You're right. It's not fair. This just sucks."

Then we just sat in silent bewilderment together, knowing we both felt the depths of dismay beyond words. I pleaded with my future self to be as patient and gentle with my mother as she was being with me. In that moment, she was the best treatment I could imagine: emotionally present. Validating. Real.

———

The next morning, in a heavily Christian city with nothing to do, she and I agreed to the only activity that made sense: church! Since she had thrown off religion after her own dogmatic Seventh-day Adventist childhood, and Dad's religion was the outdoors, my brother and I were exposed to minimal religious service while growing up. When I studied abroad in Wolverhampton, England as a romantic and lost twenty-year-old, church became an unexpected refuge for me. Lonely, I would wander around the unglamorous town between classes until I found something worth my attention; at night, it was cheesy bars with the new friends I only kind of liked, and during the day, it was the towering St. Peter's Parish church, built in the fifteenth century. I'd open the gigantic doors in between services and slip into a pew, taking in the high ceilings, stained glass, and reverent stillness. The space held an undeniable peace I couldn't find anywhere else in my youthful confusion. And my overwhelmed heart would soften. My insecurities would suddenly feel received by a greater presence, giving me permission to exhale while allowing the tears to spill down my cheeks.

But the habit didn't continue when I returned home, which meant that by this Easter Sunday, neither Mom nor I had attended more than a handful of Christian services in decades, and only then when visiting relatives. It felt a bit like a tourist attraction. After reading online reviews, I found a Unitarian church nearby which promised to offer a mild and metaphorical approach to the

Resurrection. The story and idea of rising from the dead was obviously appealing, similar to how Persephone's return was appealing. Mom agreed, exclaiming with a smile, "Sure! It'll be… different! Why not?" Donning her nicest pastel T-shirt and sneakers, with me in my best yoga pants, off we went.

This 1970s church in suburban Wichita on Easter was not nearly so awe-inspiring as the English one, yet the crowd of strangers were so welcoming and the message of renewal so sweet that the end effect was not altogether different. The service was gentle, urging for social justice and hope in that lovely way that genuinely Christian messages can do so well. I didn't want to cry in the crowd though, and I didn't want to cry, again, in front of my mother. Yet here I was, broken open by my circumstances of wanting renewed life and healing, of wanting to reject death.

In between her smiles and hand-patting reassurances, Mom was crying too, which only broke me open further. I hated to see her hurting, and yet here we are in this painful situation that neither of us appeared to have the slightest control over. What we needed was grace.

———

The last week of treatment went by quickly. Dr. C continued to unearth new clues and prescribe new supplements, which I would later come to affirm were all reasonable choices to support my body. Still, symptom improvements were barely noticeable by the end of the week, puncturing my admittedly foolish hope that healing could entail a rapid reversal of symptoms. Someone wise could have sat me down and said, "Teri, darling, get real. This is a complex illness which took many factors over many years to create. You are trying to dig out of a deep hole, with dirt constantly refilling around you. Two weeks is barely enough to address a flu. It's most likely going to take some time, and hypervigilance won't help. Be patient." And it's unlikely that I would have listened; panic isn't terribly receptive to reason. Nonetheless, I reserved hope for the hefty new bag of supplements, remedies, and treatment instructions I was being sent forth with.

The Saturday after treatment ended, John flew back to retrieve me and our car for our road trip home. We dropped my mother off at the airport hours later, both she and I with tears in our eyes, not ready to say goodbye. As she wheeled her suitcases into the terminal and John started driving us away, I noticed how she was becoming slightly stooped with age, her hair more silver than before, her wrinkles deeper. *She shouldn't have to deal with this,* I thought. *This stupid illness, my ongoing resentments, the confusion, the unknowns. It's too much.*

I thought of my father; how he had started to choke up on the phone with me despite wanting to present a strong face, lacking the words to capture his big feelings. How my brother, despite all the power and training he had to rescue people in impossible situations of distress, had admitted raw fury at being completely powerless to protect his little sister from this foe. How John had looked more and more hollowed out as the months went by, like he'd had to dig even deeper into his reserves of grit to stay hopeful.

Amidst all this, did it even matter now which exact factors were responsible for this situation arising? Because here we were—it *was.* Some forces had coalesced, or for all I know, *conspired* to present us with this challenge requiring our participation and our surrender. We were again tasked to forgive over and over while still in the midst of heartbreak. Pardon each other; pardon ourselves, despite everything.

And so it is: Life marches on, imperfectly. We age; we remain in the clutches of some painful patterns and scenarios; we grow out of others. In the hands of a large, mysterious universe, one thing is clear: we won't *not* be stretched beyond our limits, ultimately broken or broken open, and to what we do not fully know. Perhaps resurrection isn't best considered a big, one-time event; perhaps we learn it in tiny movements, with tiny decisions. Amidst all of it, we choose to keep showing up, stretching our hearts and legs to rise again.

PART III:

Unburdening

9.
The Visionary Therapist

MAY 2017

During another Internet searching marathon a month before we headed for Kansas, I had found intriguing research that proposed the plant medicine ayahuasca could be a viable treatment for ALS. Apparently, the Amazonian vine which had seen increasing popularity among spiritual seekers in the West had a number of medicinal uses in addition to its psychedelic properties owed to naturally occurring dimethyltryptamine (DMT). The Swedish researcher proposing the idea, Daniel Gustafsson, studied the potential effects of entheogens for motor neuron diseases. He outlined the science behind the antioxidant and restorative actions of the various compounds found in ayahuasca, and how they work to reconnect different parts of the brain that were no longer speaking to each other—including, possibly, motor neurons. He even posted some preliminary results of a few research subjects with ALS, who had largely seen notable improvements after a few months of daily use.

Naturally, this treatment possibility sounded much more appealing than the expensive prescriptions I had been taking, exactly zero of which had offered the additional benefit of getting high and seeing new colors. So in the months leading up to our trip to Kansas, I began experimenting with microdosing a home-brewed version of the medicine, which the Internet wondrously provided the raw materials for, along with notes on preparation.

While I had no physical improvements during a couple weeks of experimentation, *something* metaphysical seemed to be taking place. Because John had been sober for decades and I had only just retired as a fairly straight-laced addictions counselor, neither of us had done full-dose psychedelics for years. But having the special brew in our home piqued our interests, and we eventually agreed to the next logical step of attending a medicine ceremony where we had structure and guidance on taking a full dose—because, *why not?* The one we found in the foothills outside Boulder was filled with young, interesting seeker-types we were pleased to meet. Yet again the experience would offer little noteworthy for either of us except further entrenching our curiosity about the medicine's promises.

I told John perhaps it was the setting; if we were in the jungle, with the people who had been trained in facilitating transformative journeys with this medicine for generations, something useful would happen eventually. After all, I argued, the Amazon region holds the raw materials of the most potent medicine chest the planet still has, so why not visit the source, turning to the indigenous healers who might know remedies for every imaginable condition? If not ayahuasca, perhaps some other little-known remedy could help, right?

And I wasn't the only one thinking this; multiple clever friends had been encouraging me to go this route for months, and one had even set up a phone call with a woman who had fully healed stage-four uterine cancer after working with ayahuasca and other plants in Peru for a couple months. Still cancer free ten years later, she shared her story and patiently answered all my questions, ending the phone call with the advice to "expect radical healing." I could have whined to John, "C'mon, everyone's doing it," but I didn't need to since he was an easy sell. He's a seeker too. And so it was that once I returned from the treatment center in Wichita, only mildly affected by treating my body with an array of clever machines, detox methods, and nutraceuticals, we agreed that deeper treatment was in order. Perhaps treating my mind and spirit in concert with my body—something ayahuasca offers, especially in the context of a good guide who sets a good container—would provide the inner tipping point I most needed; perhaps it could trigger further resolution of whichever traumas still lingered to mess with my nervous system. We reasoned that if going down could save my life, amazing; if it couldn't, at least we'd get one more adventure as a couple before I was too paralyzed to travel. And if nothing else, it would certainly prove more interesting than Kansas.

One early May afternoon soon after deciding we wanted to go to Peru, I heard a knock at our front door. Alone in the house, I ambled down the stairs as carefully as possible and opened it in time to see a bike messenger slowly pedaling away, having left a big envelope on our doorstep. I carried it upstairs, grabbed the scissors, and awkwardly cut a hole big enough to tear through the rest with weak hands. Finding only loads of cash inside, I gasped aloud. Twenties, fifties, hundreds—yet no note and no return address.

When John returned home hours later and we counted it up together, we realized it was the exact amount we'd need for a two-week retreat for both of us. Laughing with wide-eyed delight, we agreed to take it as a sign. We never would find out who sent it, but we hoped whoever it was would've approved of the unorthodox journey we were about to take with it.

—

Traveling to South America a month later was hard. While I could still walk on my own for short distances, I required a wheelchair for the four airports we needed to navigate. John had me and all our luggage, and his concern for my needs kept him busy since I could barely grasp anything by this point, which made airport tasks like handling backpacks and water bottles and IDs and shoes doubly difficult. Still, get there we did. The humid jungle air of Iquitos enveloped us before getting off the final plane.

Carlos, the director of the retreat center we chose, met us at the airport with a taxi and accompanied us to the hotel we'd stay at before traveling to the center in the morning. While the hotel staff was gracious, giving us the ground-floor room closest to reception and offering steadying arms and cleared paths, I still managed to draw curious attention from the other guests. People could tell right away by my walking sticks and stiff gait and funny voice that I was... *different*, in some disturbing way, or perhaps just professionally drunk. A few young women in the common area took to staring so hard that they tripped over themselves, or at least they did in my imagination, which was almost just as satisfying.

After a much-needed dinner of grilled chicken and fried plantains brought from the restaurant next door, we had a meet and greet scheduled with the ten other retreat participants. We ambled to the appointed juice bar across the plaza from the hotel and began the nervous introductions with the people we would get to know well over the next two weeks; they were American and European, aged twenties to fifties, including three young staff guides representing Italy, Canada, and South Africa. We were instructed to formally introduce ourselves one by one, announcing our intentions for the retreat.

Because my voice was garbled and difficult to project to a roomful of people, when my turn came, I kept it simple. "I'd like to see about saving my life… I have Lyme disease, which has become ALS. It's a scary situation. But I still think it's possible to heal."

As the introductions continued, some sweet and pithy and some disorganized and rambling, everyone shared hopes to heal some trauma or physical condition, or at least to gain insight by jumping into the unknown reaches of their psyche. The guides expressed their excitement, and without saying as much, instructed us all to buckle up. *Here we go.*

———

The morning of our departure to the jungle retreat center, John and I were excited and nervous; or, better said, I was mostly excited and John was mostly nervous. Getting my tipsy self in and out of vehicles had become especially challenging, and John would need help from others, both with my safety and comfort and with simply tracking our stuff. We would end up navigating an open-air bus (which then became two after the first one broke down), a two-hour, twelve-seat motorized boat ride up the Nanay River (complete with unexpected detours in smaller tributaries), and then a quarter-mile walk through a small village to get to our destination. Still, neither of us could hide our grins as we bounced along on the journey, taking in the colorful buildings and chickens and dogs along the way, waving at the fishermen and marveling at the lush jungle surrounding us. By the time we arrived at the Mishana village retreat center intact with all our gear accounted for, John's grinning, sweaty face betrayed both relief and accomplishment.

Over a simple lunch of vegetable soup and rice, we were introduced to the center staff and the *curandero*—alternately known as the shaman—Don Ronor. After lunch we had more time to settle in, unpack, and rest, each waiting our turn to meet with Don Ronor individually. John helped me hobble around the elevated compound of simple wood structures on plankboard walkways. We admired the thatched palm roofs overhead and peered into the thick, humming rainforest which enveloped the center. Having noted the open-air eating area with a small simple kitchen, the row of hammocks I'd need help getting in or out of, and the traditional circular *maloca* where the ceremonies would be held, John and I retired to our room to rest. Because the humidity and steady heat of the jungle made insulation and hot water unnecessary luxuries, the outfit of twin beds, wicker shelves, a lazy fan, a bathroom with a flushable toilet, and a sticky residue of bugs and sweat felt welcoming; almost cozy.

After lying around staring at the ceiling fan for a couple hours, I was summoned to the meeting with Don Ronor. Shuffling into the maloca alone, I stiffly approached the rickety wooden seat in front of him and sat down nodding a nervous hello. Keyo, the twenty-something white South African assistant guide, invited me to share more about my situation so he could translate into Spanish. I did my best to explain what I understood about the illness, expanding upon physical symptoms while Keyo translated. They both sucked down cigarette after cigarette while Don Ronor nodded and peered heavily at me, or even *through* me, reading my energy field as if it were a complex menu of potential outcomes he could manipulate for good. Or at least I hoped that's what he was doing. He said little.

That night we didn't have dinner, as a full belly can complicate the effects of the ayahuasca. Instead, John and I sat on our beds talking quietly and waited for darkness to set in before heading into the *maloca*. Earlier in the day we had each claimed a spot in the ceremony space which we would call our own for the duration of the retreat, which mostly consisted of a bare twin mattress, a greasy pillow, and some woven blankets. We also had our own purge buckets, and a roll of toilet paper for cleaning up after said purge. After mentally cataloging the other items deemed necessities—a small flashlight, an eye mask, some *agua florida* to help me ground if I'm freaking out—and noting the location of the toilet sitting behind a shower curtain at the back of the room, I tried to stay open-minded. But despite having backpacked alone on the cheap through India for three months, with all the selective dissociation that had required at the time, this present situation still stretched my comfort—especially when considering the variety of bodily fluids usually released during ceremonies, the most benign of which is rivers of sweat. If I was still a plucky 24-year-old under the illusion of invincibility, I would have just felt adventurous. But having made it to my oh-so-discerning mid-thirties by this point, I found myself wondering what happened to Kansas. *Where are we now, Toto?*

After landing in our chosen spots again and settling in, the ceremony began. Don Ronor kicked things off by smoking a special pipe and offering quiet prayer. Moments later, we were invited to sit in front of him to drink our cup of medicine, participants and assistants alike. Keyo brought me mine first so I and everyone else could avoid the slow spectacle of my unstable shuffle through the candlelit space, a thoughtful mercy. And upon first slurp I remembered just how foul the muddy brew tastes, not unlike the small doses I had already tried.

While drinking, the task seemed twofold: 1) To hide my gag response enough to not totally embarrass myself in front of the shaman and others; and 2) To then keep the liquid down, swallowing the urge to immediately spit it back out, which would be unfortunate. Then somehow withstand witnessing other participants grimacing through these steps, averting any empathetic impulses which would cause my own repeat gagging, because mirror neurons do not always work for good. Having made it that far, I could just relax—in so much as inviting hours of potentially terrifying visions and life-changing insights is relaxing.

———

The first thing I noticed after drinking was a pleasant warmth spreading through my belly. Warmth, mixed with fear and excitement, like once the roller-coaster safety bar definitively clicks into place and it's clear you're really in for the ride, like it or not. At this point, prayer was my only available seat belt: *Mercy and goodness please. That's all. Mercy and goodness.*

The space became dark and quiet once the candles were extinguished by the assistants. At some point, responding to some invisible signal, Don Ronor began to softly whistle. The sound was otherworldly, eerie, almost like a love song to the gods: forlorn, pleading, sweet. It would meander, captivating us while our grip on reality would begin to loosen. Normal thoughts slowly began lingering, morphing into more of a dreamlike consistency.

Before long, some people started to giggle. Others started to gasp, and some started purging early. Time altered, seeming not slower or faster than normal, yet—*different*, in some ungraspable way. Vibrating sensations began to arise, yet it was difficult to trace their origin, almost as if reality itself was quaking. At a certain point I'd stop questioning if I was high and realize I was, in fact, high.

While we were all growing captivated by our morphing worlds, Don Ronor began to sing *icaros*. These traditional Shipibo songs are meant to supplicate the healing process, perhaps not unlike the Buddhist chants I had long practiced that were meant to invoke clear and benevolent awareness, but much more melodic. It worked—or *something* worked, because poetic insights started rolling in quickly as reality turned both more meaningful and weird.

The theme of the night soon centered on my relationship with men. It started with my father... Of the life-long hunger of having him fully show up... Of how he simply could not in the way I wanted him to... Of how my brother could not fully fill the gap... Of how deeply this had marked me, like a hunger I would never satiate... And how the bulk of my career working with men—mostly bound by addictions and scarred by trauma—had been a doomed attempt of resolving this disconnection from the father archetype. *Wow. Oops.* And, *Of course.*

———

After a few hours of sweating through such visions, the sparks of novel insight gradually slowed. Familiar sober reality came back into view as the passage of time smoothed out. Though I already knew it felt like a decade of talk therapy and supervision had been tackled in hours of revelatory gifts, I didn't yet know what to do with all of it. I didn't yet know that I would spend hours crying the next day, grieving what I'd always known but hadn't *known* I'd known.

Once the ceremony officially ended, the guides lit the candles and had a one by one call and response with all of us to make sure we weren't still sick or overwhelmed. Some people needed help coming down, at which point one of the guides would come over and try to help them ground. John, whose spot was right next to mine, eventually leaned in and whispered, "Hey... how you doing?"

Uhhhh... uhhhh?

Eventually I croaked, "Whoa."

He chuckled. "Yeah... Right?"

After I slowly sat up, we shared the briefest of reports. Others began grouping up and dramatically telling stories about what they had seen and experienced. It felt like something along the lines of a future reality ayahuasca TV show, so I hobbled unsteadily back to our hut with my arm over John's shoulder. While sleep would prove hard to find, it made sense to lie quietly and reflect on what had just happened, taking turns sharing some thoughts. Around sunrise we got quiet and finally nodded off.

A few hours later, we woke hungry for breakfast and ready to connect, so we stumbled blinking to the dining area to greet the tableful of our bleary-eyed new friends. After getting help from John with spooning together a full plate, I dug in with appetite, listening while others shared stories from the night before. Someone had taken a ride on a flying green dragon; someone saw the root cause of their terrible chronic pain; someone spilled their puke bucket on their bed. At least one person overestimated their capacity, drank too much, and ended up in a hell realm for nearly six hours. And so our journeys began.

We were to do ceremonies every other evening, and in the off times there was lots of space to read, talk, lounge in hammocks, and eat unlimited tiny wild bananas. Largely it was a restful affair. On most days we'd all have a turn in special steam baths, customized with plant allies chosen for our individual needs. Our task was simply to relax and breathe deeply while sitting over a giant pot of fragrant, scalding-hot water. Self-conscious about my so-skinny bikinied body until covered by the tarp that turned the whole thing into a sauna, I'd sweat rivers and pray that these plants would be able to trigger the changes that all my previous attempts at healing had not.

We had a few group activities which had to do with purging of some sort, all to further detox our bodies of long-held physical or energetic burdens. A few days in, all ten of us stood in a line in the grass behind the *maloca*, quickly gulping cup after cup of bitter plant purgatives until it provoked us to vomit. It was an especially entertaining affair, complete with absurd cheerleading for each other: "Drink! Drink! Drink! Go! Faster! Go! You got it! Oh, here it comes! Yeah! Whew! [clapping] Nice spill."

John had been purging generously from both ends during ceremonies, a fact which had on each occasion triggered both my sympathy and childish amusement. *Tee hee, "Blechhh."* Meanwhile, nothing was making me vomit, including ayahuasca. I grew strangely jealous watching everyone else spew their brews, while I could only sit there, dry-heaving pathetically. *Why am I the only weirdo who can't puke? Let go, Teri! Let! Go!*

Meanwhile, Keyo would check in with me often, offering new potions and plant tinctures placed into recycled plastic bottles, explaining in detail how they work both on physical and energetic levels, and giving me pep talks to bolster my confidence in the treatment. He seemed to have taken a liking to me and John and became invested in helping as much as he could, confessing that John's obvious devotion to me was acting as a teaching to him. We both fell for his caring attention, and I was reminded of how humility makes for a true healer.

One morning over breakfast, after having thoroughly recounted the story with John, I was excited to get to share with Keyo what had happened in the prior evening's journey, in case what I'd learned could help him better treat people like me in the future. I'd already shared with him how I'd seen my body was filled with toxic metals like that bad cop in Terminator, and was shown that getting them *out* would be necessary for a chance of physical recovery. But after the last journey, I now felt I understood why my illness, and the complex of illnesses related to deeply entrenched chronic infections in general, are incredibly difficult to treat: we simply don't give them enough credit.

So I told my story: how, midway into the evening, I had a vision of the illness inside me as a whole. It was alive. If it was an infection, it was a super infection, or more accurately, a form of possession. It appeared as a coiled snake or serpent, filling the space between my pelvis and throat. This entity had effectively merged itself with my DNA, which meant that every attempt to kill or weaken it also weakened me. It was undeniably intelligent, growing and morphing in response to all my treatment interventions, steadily becoming craftier and trickier as a result. I saw that it was both feminine and masculine in nature, meaning it knew how to hide and yield when necessary, while also knowing how to attack and feed from me—the ultimate parasite.

As I looked back on it, a day removed and with much more of my wits about me, this made sense. I was learning that ayahuasca offers an invitation to get below ordinary waking consciousness and become aware of the soulful, interconnected, sacred unifying principle of life itself. It becomes undeniable that all living beings are intelligent, have their own language, and can communicate to us humans, if only we'd learn how to listen. While it felt self-evident, it also felt spooky to realize the extent of sentient consciousness dancing around us all the time, just below our awareness. *Say whaaat?*

And here I was, seeing that the illness itself appeared to have its own sentience, its own life force—or, at least, a sophisticated enough ability to feed off mine. (Within another year I would run across new scientific research explaining this exact phenomenon of stealth chronic infections which build synergistically, effectively turn off the immune system, alter the nervous system, and hinder normal detox functions, rendering standard treatment approaches such as antibiotics, antivirals, and antifungals laughably inadequate. But at the time, this vision of the illness as a conscious *force* felt like a revelation.)

I explained to Keyo that clearly, the energy of the illness was even more intelligent—and therefore, more formidable—than I had ever imagined. And yet, not knowing what to do with this super being inside me during the ceremony, I opted for the best thing I could think of in the moment: fight with the fucker. I wanted this thing *out*. So after sweating for hours, struggling to extricate myself from its death grip, I won the battle—or at least, that's what I wanted to believe, and it's what I reported to Keyo.

In retrospect, I now see the conquer as wishful fantasy; it would not be so easy to win my freedom, even if ayahuasca could show me the true nature of my unwelcome guest. This thing was now a part of me, having woven itself into my gene expression, and I'd already been shown that brute force wouldn't do it. My approach would need to be wiser than that.

———

In addition to the dining-table debriefs, we had a discussion group as part of the retreat. I looked forward to this because my geeky therapist-self loved group process, and I knew magical opportunities for integration happen in group discussions when the container is strong.

The group began with Keyo inviting us to share in a circle to check in about our experiences so far. As a shameless connoisseur of group process, an old, familiar electricity ran through my veins at getting a chance to critically evaluate another leader at work. I watched as Keyo received our shares skillfully, adding supportive comments as necessary, mostly seeming to trust our own judgment for how and what to share. He had enough sensitivity and presence to hold the process naturally; I silently approved.

The young Italian guide—we'll call her Gabriella—provided contrast to Keyo's gentle methodology. Taking a deep breath between rapid cigarette puffs, she dove into a long, confusing, heady intervention whenever anyone finished speaking. "See, it's clear that you need to learn to let go more…" or, "You're not looking at this correctly. You need to transcend…" or, "It's important for you to learn how to relax…" I fantasized about suggesting to her it'd be okay for her to relax a bit too; *we'll probably make it.*

At the conclusion of one of her lecture-ventions, John took his turn. He described some of the insights he had had during the ceremonies, including the non-existence of space and time as we tend to understand them, and revelations on the nature of his relationships throughout life and how to better allow their flourishing. The guides thanked him, Gabriella got some words in, and everyone turned to me.

Pausing a moment before speaking, I slowly began searching for the words to describe my ceremony experiences. So far, my journeys had taken different tones each time, newly connecting neurological pathways which illuminated relevant spheres of my life. There had been downloads on my health, relationship patterns, long-held fears, and nagging hang-ups, all of which validated physical, psychological, or spiritual realities which I had never grasped before yet suddenly become glaringly obvious. In that way, I knew the medicine had been serving as a wise and compassionate therapist/doctor, offering not only a deeper perspective on my life but helping expand my sense of agency in giving me the conscious choice of how to live based on the new information.

But there was one theme in particular where I felt the most vulnerable, lost, and raw, which I decided to go with sharing to the group. I began by describing how, in the third ceremony, I had seen and felt myself emerging from deep underground into the daylight, suggesting emergence into new life—like Persephone returning to Earth. I shared how this was so encouraging that I buzzed for hours the next day, inwardly claiming my rightful place on a healing track.

Taking a deep breath, I then shared how this excitement had faded after the next ceremony, where I had an ominous vision of being on a boat designed for ALS patients, set to go over a cliff and fall to our deaths within three years. I shared how despite knowing the deaths in journeys were often only symbolic, the visceral doom accompanying this vision had punctured my previous encouragement—that these messages, which seemed to fundamentally conflict in outcome and feel, left me grappling for meaning, wondering how much choice I still had in setting my life's direction. I mentioned a bardo-like feeling of walking between worlds, unsure of whether to orient toward life or death, wanting so badly to trust the whole experience and surrender to it, but not yet knowing what it was I could trust. I shared how, despite knowing the value of surrender, I still very much preferred to recover my health and live.

The room seemed to crackle with presence. As I spoke my last words, I felt that unique satisfaction that comes from being deeply witnessed by a caring group; of being held by the reverent attention of others. And I *had* been—with one notable exception.

With barely a second passing after I concluded, as if we were in a televised political debate, Gabriella jumped in. "I'm sorry, but I'm going to be straight with you," she announced, taking a deep inhale.

Oh God, I thought, *please don't.*

Barely catching her breath, she jumped into a rapidly paced admonition of my every word. I titrated my attention by staring outside and breathing into the toes I was newly interested in wiggling, but to my dismay I still managed to hear every third sentence or so, which was stern, and went like this: "Your misery is your own choice…"

And, "I know quadriplegics who feel gratitude with every breath they take; they find a way to get over themselves and find happiness…"

And, "If you only learned how to train your mind, I mean *really* train it, you'd find nothing to complain about…"

And, "Your happiness is waiting for you, always, *always, always,* you just have to choose it…"

In summary, I needed to raise my vibration, and let go, and lighten up.

And… mic drop.

———

Once back in our room with the door closed, I flopped on the bed and shot a look at John. "Uhh… what did you think of that little intervention I was just served?" He snorted and paused, collecting his thoughts. I hoped he was in the mood for one of his damning rants, one skill of his I have always found delightful—especially when we'd agreed upon its target, and it wasn't me.

"Well… I know you don't need protection," he said. "But it took everything I had to not let her have it. What a joke."

I giggled, feeling playful. "Please say more, wise one."

Before he could say more, I continued, snarling, "Did she even hear what I said? I've been to enough twelve-step meetings to know what self-pity sounds like. Did it actually sound like I was complaining?"

John opened his mouth to speak, and I continued, "I wasn't complaining. But really, who the hell cares if I was, right? Ms. Answers with her functional limbs and rosy future got a little too uppity. Am I right?"

He jumped in. "What you were saying was honest and real. It was beautiful. And she took a big wordy shit on it. She was desperate to be the star of the show, the one getting the attention, departing spiritual wisdom from on high to the rest of us like we're idiots for being mortals and having real feelings about life, but instead, she just came off looking like an ass."

Aaahhh. My heart melted.

During the swaying hammock sessions of the following week, I tried to unpack her line of thinking more. I knew there was *some* abstract truth in *some* of her words; if one only releases attachment to their plans and beholds reality as it arises with gratitude, mining its lessons, a certain workability and resilience can be found in even relatively terrible situations. But this wasn't abstract for me. This was *my* limbs, *my* voice, *my* life—and my timeline to find acceptance. Are we to not have "negative" feelings about the threat of death? Are we to somehow skip over the very human emotions of grief, fear, anger, etc. when our imagined future is stripped from us? If we could let go so easily, what might that say about how much we had loved what we lost? And how is telling someone to "just get over it" enlightened, even if you supposedly know someone who has miraculously gotten over it, which by itself is debatable?

To me her attitude served as a shiny example of spiritual bypassing, the seductive line of thinking which says, "If only we transcend our human desires and difficult emotions and developmental needs, we'll become free of lower earthly things and therefore more spiritual." By this point, having been either a therapist, group facilitator, meditation instructor, or twelve-step sponsor for hundreds of people over a number of years, I was familiar with the urge to turn to a fuzzy, feel-good interpretation of spirituality in the hope we might not have to fully confront the hard edges of our emotional or relational lives. It's very, very common, and the influx of New Age philosophy into pop culture only throws gas on the flames of collective dissociation.

But I knew we humans weren't robots. We have soft bellies and hearts, and naturally come equipped with a wide emotional range and basic life-preserving mammalian desire. Many people—quadriplegic or not—put on a strong face after trauma or loss because they feel they should, but that doesn't necessarily capture the true, fluctuating nuance of how they feel. And I can only imagine those who find genuine acceptance after significant losses do so through committed emotional, mental, and perhaps spiritual work over the course of months or years, if they are fortunate enough to have the time and support to do so. Emotional integration and resilience-building are spiraling processes which require ongoing tending; there's no cognitive switch we can flip to make trauma and loss disappear somehow. Rather than denying our heartbreak, we can honor it, all the while affirming our new outlook and perhaps even cultivating an ultimate view of trustworthiness and workability of the whole shebang.

Long before I ever encountered Gabriella, I was becoming increasingly protective of all the grieving people out there who have been blasted by arrogant comments from others about how they needed to shape up and get over it, since there's a difference between skillfully sensing *what* needs to be said *when* and blowing someone's head off with your own "spiritual wisdom." But I was also once naive in my presumed solutions to everyone else's pain and had held unrealistic expectations to drop difficult feelings on many an occasion. Even my wandering into that bookstore so soon after diagnosis, praying for a message which might soften the blow of my new prognosis, had a certain bypassing desire to it. Perhaps the slap I got instead ("ALS is the worst possible thing") was simply reality's way of reminding me, "Honey, you've got some more work to do before making anything feel-good out of this. Go home and feel your feelings first. All of them."

So I chalked her comments up to her own yet-to-mature ability to honestly behold mortality and loss, and resolved to largely steer clear of her. Meanwhile, John happily indulged my urges to poke fun at what she had said throughout the rest of the retreat. I realized two things: *God, I love this man.* And *God, it feels good to luxuriate in suspiciously non-spiritual, unapologetically un-evolved, totally un-transcended mockery sometimes.*

Once back in the taxi in Iquitos, headed for the airport, I held John's hand. "Are we making the right decision? Having me stay longer without you?" I asked.

John slowly nodded, "I think so. You need more time getting treatment, and this is probably the best place for it."

I agreed; an extended stay beyond the retreat dates was not an option the first center offered, but the staff at the new center where I had booked an open-ended stay were notified of my condition and assured me they could accommodate my needs.

He squeezed my hand, again saying he wished he could stay, reminding me it was good that Keyo would be near enough, and that I could come home as soon as I wanted. I nodded and gazed out the window, making the rest of the ride quiet and bittersweet. I was excited to get to stay in Peru for more adventure, yet apprehensive about doing it without my best friend providing physical and emotional steadying by my side.

Once we arrived, John helped me and my stuff from one moto-taxi to another, then we turned to each other with tears in our eyes. We both knew neither of us were sure if parting was the right choice. But he had a plane to catch, so after kissing me goodbye he turned to walk into the terminal, the sliding glass doors swallowing him whole. I missed him terribly and immediately. Now it was just me, my two bags, the mercy of strangers, and an unknown fate ahead—along with the sentient, living serpent I had come to know as my illness.

10.
A Doubter's Flirt
with Faith

JUNE 2017

Something surprising happened after the moto-taxi and driver began whisking me toward the next retreat center—something even Gabriella might have applauded. Our little vehicle sputtered and weaved, dodging stray dogs and taxis and schoolchildren and motorbikes moving in every conceivable direction across the highway, us inhaling cacophonies of pungent black exhaust. And as I swayed in the vinyl back seat, clutching my backpack as best I could over the bumps, trying to prevent my unsteady body from falling out of the doorless side, something within me released. Not a minor, *I'll-get-to-the-retreat-center-in-one-piece-and-it'll-be-okay* kind of release, but in a major, *ohmygod-life-is-fundamentally-trustworthy* sort of release. And it all became inexplicably, wholly perfect, as if I had somehow slipped into a jet stream of awakened, blissful awareness.

Suddenly I got it: even if we were to crash—a reasonably possible scenario as we hurtled through Iquitos—and my hiking poles and little purple backpack and rolling suitcase and vulnerable human body were to go flying into the great beyond, it would be completely... *fine*. No matter the injuries, no matter if I died. As a consciousness I was safe, and there was nothing to try to control within the relative constructions of good/bad or right/wrong. I saw that underneath my desire to take the reins on reality, trying to force it to conform to my wishes and respect my fears, there lies the possibility of pure, unadulterated freedom. So suddenly, I could relax—which is what I did, allowing my grips to loosen and my body to unclench, just luxuriating in the sensations of the unstable ride.

It's hard to describe the delight this deep letting go brought; it was not unlike the energetic download I had received shortly after diagnosis on relaxing into the freefall, except this one felt ecstatic and colorful, the inner glow lasting a good ten minutes before easing up. It was as if an accumulation of the ceremony experiences spontaneously bubbled through to my sober life as a blessing, or a cosmic orgasm—or, as I would learn later, an unprecedented dopamine surge.

By the time we turned off the highway onto the final dirt road leading to the center, my normal state of self-protection and separation started again tugging at the corners of my mind. Yet the experience would live sewn into my being, bringing me peace whenever I recalled it in subsequent months. *Whoa. There is truly no problem in the big picture. No problem at all, ever.*

When we arrived at the new center, the driver unloaded my suitcase and offered me a steadying arm as I climbed out. Upon entering the main dining hall, I was soon met by Julien, the center director who had been anticipating my arrival. After greeting me warmly in his French-accented English, he said he wished to talk more once I'd finished the lunch the cook had left for me.

Twenty minutes later, I'd had all the chicken, rice, and avocado I could stomach and pushed my plate aside. Julien sat down across from me and lit up a cigarette, asking me to tell him more about my illness and my intentions for my stay. Sharing with him the treatments I had been doing at the other center, none of which had triggered noticeable physical effects, and how Don Ronor had offered minimal feedback on my condition, I wanted to know what treatment ideas they might have. Between slow, thoughtful puffs, Julien said it would be important for the shaman, Pablo, to see me in ceremony before they could provide a treatment plan.

Grabbing my bag and inviting me to follow, he walked outside. Quickly realizing his normal pace would outdo my unsteady shuffle, he took a deep breath and slowed himself. We walked along a sandy cleared path toward a compound of six standalone apartments. Red doors complemented the cheery yellow walls, all roofed by corrugated metal—which I'd soon learn would emit a gunshot-loud crack when fruit from the adjacent palms would fall onto them.

My room was big and bright inside, the light dappled only by the bell-shaped white flowers climbing up just outside the window.

After setting my suitcase down on the woven rug partially hiding the concrete floor, Julien accepted my request to help me unzip my bag and unpack a little, adding that he or other staff would be able to walk me back to my room after the ceremonies if needed. And with that, he left me alone to settle in.

After tending to the details of unpacking, including setting up my art supplies on my new desk and loads of supplements and tinctures on my new bookshelf, I lay down on the bed to relax before the evening ceremony, taking in my clean, spacious surroundings. I decided I had made the right decision to stay. *Definitely. Probably.*

As I rested, I thought of the unlikely turns my life had taken since I first wished for life surprises. How, under Reggie's influence, I had suspected psychedelics were a cheater's substitution for the "real" spiritual work of meditation, yet here I was to great benefit; how I had assumed prior to getting sick that radical healing could be rather straightforward with enough willingness, when it was turning out to be anything but; how it turned out surrender and relaxation may be less a conscious decision and more a gracious blessing when the conditions are right to receive.

———

At nightfall I strapped on my headlamp and stepped with my poles onto the dark path to greet the *maloca* for the first time. Despite being lit only by a few candles, it was clear upon entering the space was beautiful, and well constructed of rich dark hardwood. The shadow of compassion goddess Kwan Yin flickered off the center support beam behind her, adding texture to the simple shrine.

Julien was already there waiting, as was Pablo, the shaman. Pablo was a cheery-looking Peruvian in his forties, quiet, showing laughter wrinkles in his face and nursing a hand-rolled cigarette. In between his own quick drags, Julien translated introductions between us and said he'd already explained my situation to Pablo. He then showed me to my mattress, complete with my own selection of mildly grimy pillows, and told me we'd check in after the ceremony. I opted to lie down and try to get comfortable; because I had requested a break from ingesting ayahuasca, my only task would be to stay awake and present for what unfolded that evening. I then promptly fell asleep.

After an uneventful morning and lunch the next day, I finally sat down with Pablo and Julien in the dining hall. I was eager to hear the mystical download that Pablo had received during the ceremony about what I was facing. Trying my best to understand his rapid Spanish, all my gringo ear could make out was *muy*, very, and *mal*, bad.

Sucking on his cigarette, Julien then took a deep breath and translated. "During the ceremony last night... um... it looks like... Well, does your family have any ties to the mafia?"

"What?" I gasped.

He was serious. They both stared at me expectantly as I stared back, incredulous.

My mind reeled. Some male members of my extended family had antisocial tendencies, just enough to collect guns, fear immigrants, and hold earnest allegiance to Fox News. But they were never organized enough for organized crime, or arousing significant bad juju from a cunning enemy. At least, so I had always thought. "Uh... I don't think so..." I replied.

"Okay. Well, it looks like someone very powerful has had really, um… negative intentions toward you," Julien said. "And maybe related to your family."

"Really?" I asked, trying to keep my mind open.

Julien continued. "Yeah. Pablo says someone has cursed you, and this is at the root of your illness. He says it was someone with very dark energy, who may have even entered your house once. It's powerful, this energy. Very bad. They may be in a rival family, or a dark lineage of some sort."

Now this was interesting. It could explain the parasitic serpent vision, I thought. Though not ready to land on feeling creeped out—or hopeful that we were finally getting somewhere—I flashed on the memory of something unexpected the medical intuitive had told me almost a year prior, along these same lines. After explaining how she saw the Lyme disease in my nervous system, and the heavy metals, she had said there was one additional significant factor she saw underlying the symptoms:

"Yes. Let me see… Do you work in public service of some sort…? Yes… I'm seeing a young man… looks like in his twenties. You told him you didn't want to serve him, or couldn't work with him for some reason… He was terribly upset… yeah… Yes, and it looks like your ALS symptoms started shortly after… Mmmhmm… Oh… oh… a curse. It looks like he got you good."

A shiver had rippled through me and my hair had stood on end. Out of the hundreds of clients I had worked with that same year, I knew immediately who she must be referring to: a cocky white man in his early twenties who had been court ordered to one of my DUI treatment groups. The first time I'd met him I'd had a strange sense that he hurt people on purpose, and he was just getting started—a sense that had reliably given me shivers every time he was in the room with me. Woman-hating bitterness had exuded from his very pores, and a force field of sociopathic negativity surrounded him like a dark aura. After three or four groups of observing him stare me down with murderous, humiliating intent, blatantly ignoring my reminders about group guidelines and occasionally throwing insults in my direction with a sick sparkle in his eyes, I'd had enough. Under instructions from the agency director, I called him one day and told him not to come to group again, and furthermore, to find a different agency for treatment. Not surprisingly, he was outraged.

For the next month I was frightened to ride my bike to work, as I had images of him attacking me while unlocking it after an evening group. I sensed if there was ever a client of mine bitter and spiteful enough to curse me or come after me, it would have been him. And sure enough, my hand started weakening about a month after I fired him from treatment.

Prior to the call with the intuitive, I didn't believe in curses. The idea seemed archaic and superstitious, an affront to our spiritual sovereignty. But after the call, I decided to research the idea in more depth, to try to better understand the purported mechanics of them. I wanted to know, did the person doing the cursing always know what they were doing, as in studying black magic? Was a ritual involved? How was the curse transmitted through time and space? What makes a cursee an open target for the cursor? And, once infected with said curse, how did you then break free of it?

The most reasonable explanation I came across—in the very trustworthy world of random blogs, that is—went something like this: No, people are not always consciously aware of "cursing" someone else, at least not as in, *I am going to practice voodoo on that person and do some weird ritual to make them grow spots.* It's more likely that they would be feeling a powerful malevolent intent, thinking about how they'd like to control that person or see them suffer—almost like a negative, transpersonal manifestation practice. If the recipient of those negative thought waves then found themselves feeling vulnerable, unbalanced, unprotected, etc.—think me, alone at night behind my office, heart pounding and holding my breath while fumbling with my bike lock—then the energy of victimization had a chance to lodge in their subtle field and weaken them. I found this believable enough, especially knowing how this man had already given me the willies so easily.

The intuitive ended up referring me to a colleague in Nevada who was apparently skilled at removing these things and warned me that I wouldn't want just anyone working on it—presumably because many energy workers would be out of their league. I took the guy's number and called a couple times, yet he'd never responded. Due to my ongoing distraction of pursuing physical treatments, and my own stubborn doubts that a curse could be a major driving force in my illness, I'd dropped the pursuit.

But this fresh report forced me to revisit the possibility. Perhaps there was still something heavy attached to me which Don Ronor couldn't see—or wouldn't touch. Still, the description Pablo was giving here sounded different. That young client had certainly not been inside my house, nor knew my family. Could it be the same person—the same curse? Or was my ancestral lineage carrying some wicked energy which I was unwittingly bearing the brunt of?

I knew of the growing body of research hinting toward cross-generational transmission of trauma, and the little I knew of my recent ancestry hinted toward a fair share of depression and addiction, poverty and dislocation, estrangement and violence. I thought of how a few years prior to diagnosis, and in my voracious therapeutic curiosity, I had sprung for a "family constellations" workshop despite all warnings of it being mere pseudoscience. During my turn as the focus client, once my whole extended family was "accounted for" in the room by surrogate participants who energetically stood in for them, I suddenly felt inexplicably, overwhelmingly heavy and tired—so tired that I lay down on the carpet and nearly fell asleep in the middle of the whole thing. I could barely move. The facilitator was admittedly stumped about how to work with my very ill "family system," and I pedaled my bike home to John bummed I had spent $150 and a Saturday on it with no sense of benefit. Perhaps I was holding an old dark fatigue in my very bones.

My mind kept spinning. I wondered if Pablo had just translated the devastation of my symptoms into the cultural and spiritual framework he knew, since curses are a not uncommon explanation for misfortune within the Shipibo culture; I wondered if I should translate it metaphorically, since the diagnosis itself certainly felt like a psychological hex, near impossible to overcome. I'd wonder over the coming days until exhausted, knowing I'd never find the answers through my own left-brain analysis. I only hoped the coming weeks of shamanic attention to this mystery would provide more information, and that my only task would be to observe how my body responded.

———

Because there were no scheduled activities other than the ceremonies and the meals, it didn't take long to realize I had plenty of free time to fill. In my previous body I would have taken advantage of the unfamiliar jungle setting by taking exploratory walks beyond the center or dips in the nearby pond, but that physical ability was no longer an option on my own. In fact, walking between the dining hall and my room a couple times a day, accompanied by some gentle stretching while sitting outside and batting away the mosquitos, felt like all the movement I could muster.

So I sat a lot. The coming weeks would find me sitting in my room, willing my hands to grip markers well enough to color landscapes in my coloring book. Sitting on the wooden bench in front of my apartment, witnessing the diverse plant life all around populated by butterflies, stray cats, and the occasional puppy in search of ankles to bite. Sitting in the dining hall and reading Haruki Murakami or utopian fantasy tomes old participants had left, made greasy by the bug dust and humidity. When the Internet service was working, I'd sit and talk to John or family over video chat, pausing sometimes to show them the deafening intensity of rain that can sweep through the jungle in a flash. I'd sit with the other participants or staff, trying to shake the lonely feeling of facing something enormous that they were not.

But mostly, I sat and thought. About my past, about how I could find myself here, about what I wanted for my future if I was fortunate enough to get my life back. About what I needed to do to finally reverse the disease. About what it would mean if I could not.

Meanwhile, I sat down with Pablo and Julien regularly to assess my progress. Pablo said the plant treatments were making me strong, and his work on the curse appeared to be loosening its grip, especially since he had called in two additional visiting shamans to help him with it during the two weeks of ceremonies: my own energetic counterterrorism taskforce. Despite wanting to believe that I was getting stronger, I repeatedly confessed that I was slowly getting weaker. I'd then get a stern talking-to about the need to stick with the treatment plan and fully believe in it, otherwise I had no chance. "Faith!" they chorused like a bossy mantra, shaking their heads at me.

I understood their arguments. It's common for us human-folk to believe our conditions are uniquely impossible to live with or recover from. But by this time, I'd known what it felt like to heal from difficult physical problems: dark climate depression, nagging infections, long-held sports injuries, hormonal imbalances. Once certain conditions were put in place, whether those were treatments, supplements, sunshine, rest, or lifestyle changes, something inside would usually begin to reknit, and the visceral feeling of reintegration seemed to loan momentum to physical recovery. Since I had always trusted in my ability to overcome these conditions, it was easy to look back and confuse correlation with causation, i.e., "faith equals healing" and—if I wasn't the one personally housed in a body disabled by ALS—therefore assume healing was *always* simply a matter of commitment.

But this current quandary felt different. How was I to believe I was physically healing when I didn't have any evidence that it was true or even possible? The only evidence I had was symbolic or anecdotal, and by this time I'd had too many unrealized omens to put unquestioned faith in any of them. And my pet peeve for others who quickly ascribed meaning to "signs" had only grown as I'd waded further into the grips of disease. I'd think, *Hold up. How do you know that feather isn't just a feather? When is that "11:11" a communication from the cosmos, and when is it just pattern recognition plus confirmation bias, like seeing Volkswagens everywhere after wanting to buy one and taking it as a sign to act?*

After all, while some argue that it's important not to overthink a sacred venture like healing, there's still a time and place for exercising discernment, for bringing your head along with your heart. It's hard to ignore the examples of deeply faithful people throughout history who didn't heal from whatever ailed them; are we to believe they all failed? In some religious or spiritual circles, sober thinking sadly falls by the wayside too often by people wanting to interpret the future (and the intentions of the divine) via their own hopes. But I now knew you could only have the rug pulled out from under your rosy wishes so many times before learning to question the tidy conclusions, thereby gaining a type of galactic street smarts.

Still, I'd wonder, was doubt preventing my healing? There were periods when I "knew" I was getting stronger, either through convincing meditations, or ceremonies, or positive temporary responses to treatments. Yet these results never lasted; every time, my weakness would ultimately grow, thereby entrenching my doubt. I recommitted in faith over and over, but my commitment only lasted until the extent of my disability was once again in my face: using the bathroom, holding utensils, dressing, talking, walking, each week a bit weaker than the week before. Holding on to faith when direct evidence invalidated it was like shuffling along a razor's edge. Perhaps from the strength of the deadly nocebo of the terminal diagnosis, I now needed to feel my recovery in real time before believing it: the opposite of faith. Cue the gurus and preachers on planets near and far shaking their heads in collective disapproval. *Womp-womp.*

Yet behind the scenes of my questions about recovery was a quieter type of transmission brewing. Slowly, I was beginning to develop more trust in my overall pattern of survival; that somehow, moment by moment, I'd made it this far, and maybe I could therefore just keep going, moment by moment. This allowed me to question, *What if each difficult moment we humans survive can better prepare us to survive the next difficult moment? What if grief, and even disability itself, somehow becomes easier to deal with, more friendly, more familiar over time? Does it make sense to anticipate hardship and burden ourselves with defeat when we don't know what the future holds, or how it might feel when it arrives?* Maybe the only faith I could have was the faith in my ability to keep showing up, adapting, and learning, no matter the outcome.

———

With these questions as a backdrop, I continued nightly dips into ayahuasca. This center offered ceremonies five nights a week, so there was little time to integrate one evening's experiences before heading into the next one. An example: one night I'd have a mighty revelation on love being the very fabric of existence itself. The day after, I was gushing with blissful warmth toward *everything*, a bit hungover from a passionate romp with the universe. That same evening, not sure what else could possibly be unveiled, I dutifully took the cup from Pablo yet again.

After sipping the muddy medicine, rearranging my seat, and feeling the now-familiar warmth spread outward from my core, I soon began witnessing my grasp on conventional reality start to quiver. My awareness rearranged itself. And within another hour of progressively loosening associations, I once again found myself gasping at what was uncovered. Like in so many other journeys I took, it was less a vision and more of a *knowing* that sprung on me seemingly out of nowhere.

We don't die. We change form.

I saw how, at the death of our bodies, something—our essence, our soul—just peacefully slips out to head for a new location. I saw how consciousness itself is unbroken and indestructible. I saw how relieving this is for humans to realize upon our deaths. And something in me relaxed deeply. *What freedom! This life is just one small experience among an unending journey of experiences, and at its conclusion I will simply slip out of my "Teri" body and relax once more into a larger existence.* This reinforced what the moto-taxi ride had shown me about letting go; once again, everything on the soul level was ultimately "all good."

———

The next day, after showering and walking back from lunch in the dining hall, I entered my room in a particularly good mood, reveling in a new level of trust in existence. I shuffled toward my bookcase for my post-meal ritual of supplements and tinctures with an extra bounce in my step.

As I reached toward the top shelf for my vitamin tray, I was greeted by a baby lizard standing guard just beyond my outstretched hand. It was maybe two inches long, about as cuddly and unthreatening as any reptile is capable of looking, yet the surprise of it was just strong enough to knock my stiff, spastic legs out of balance. During the slow-motion fall backward, I had enough time to think, *Oh dang, this is going to hurt.*

Although my butt must have hit the floor first, it felt as if the back of my head was the only thing that made contact. And it hit the concrete fast, with a loud thumping crack. (Pause. Emptiness. Shock.) *Shit, what just happened? Oh shit, that just happened.* Blood started pouring out of my head. Only upon rolling to my side and propping up on my shoulder did I realize just how much.

Fortunately, my voice was still strong enough to belt out a "Help! Hellllp!"

A friend heard me first from her room and came running. She opened my door, saw me on the floor in a growing puddle of blood, said, "Oh shit," and yelled, "Juuuliiienn!"

He arrived within twenty seconds, saw the blood, said, "Oh shit! I'm getting help. Hold on!"

Within another minute, Julien and the staff medic returned, carrying buckets and gauze and towels and soap. Julien helped me carefully sit up, my shirt and hair a bloody mess. The medic went to work to try to stop the blood flow by holding a towel to my head while Julien sat in front of me asking me questions, trying to keep me conscious. Before long we were accompanied by other staff who went to work cleaning up the large pool of blood and handing the medic gauze and buckets of fresh water. People ran in and out trying to arrange for a moto-taxi to take me to the nearest hospital. Some staff started to pray over me in Shipibo. I noted my favorite tank top was now grossly tattooed by my blood. *Shit!*

Taking in this new turn of events, I looked at Julien and asked, "Why must my life be so hard?" My humor was so dry that it didn't register with him until I giggled. He then let out a surprised laugh in response to my bemused question, which only made me giggle more. Soon the whole room was laughing, all relieved that I was at least okay enough to make fun of the situation. "*Poco... poco,* uh, lizard," I said, not knowing the word for reptile in Spanish, yet wanting to explain. Everyone then laughed harder as my story was translated.

Before long, the blood flow slowed enough for the medic to feel confident in the current round of gauze and bandages, and with he and Julien each taking an arm, they carried my limp, still-shocked body down the path and sandwiched me into the moto-taxi. With a dramatic flourish, the driver started the vehicle, and away we puttered.

By now I was having fun, or at least the sensation of fun, which was undoubtedly adrenaline plus the joy of being conscious. My head was finally starting to hurt though, and having seen so much blood loss, I thought this might be the beginning of my end. But since I had had my insights about death the night before in ceremony, I felt free and largely unconcerned. Although I had a sad pang that John and family would be upset at me dying far away in the jungle, I wasn't afraid; mostly, I felt fortunate to be on an adventure in a moto-taxi, knowing that even if my body was about to die, my journey would continue. The realization that I didn't have to worry about anything was freeing, so I rode to the emergency room with a big dumb grin on my face.

By the time we arrived at the hospital thirty minutes later, my head was throbbing. The medical staff urgently asked Julien question after question in Spanish while wheeling me between various rooms and collecting more attendants. While cleaning my wound, they told Julien I would need the bigger hospital in town to do a CT scan to see if my skull had cracked. So after a quick checkout process, we piled back in the moto-taxi and puttered further into the city.

The adrenaline started to wear off around the time we arrived at the second hospital. Luckily, the CT scan would soon show my skull was fully intact. This was a bit of a miracle. But a much bigger miracle was the fact that the charges for all of the medical services I'd received that day amounted to just $70, with no questions about insurance or lengthy forms to fill out, which left me wondering for a moment if John and I should move to Peru. These are apparently the kind of practical musings that still arise in the midst of life and death.

———

Having extended my stay by five weeks, I began feeling increasingly restless. Despite reassurances by the staff, I wasn't convinced that this help was getting me any further. Weeks spent working on the curse, or whatever it was, had not made a noticeable difference for me. While the ayahuasca had gifted me with some profound insights and greatly reduced my fear of death, it had not reknit my nervous system or motor neurons as I had hoped. My disability had grown. Many of my supplements from home were now growing mold on them from the humidity. My legs and arms were a treasure map of bug bites which I didn't have the willpower to stop scratching. But mostly, I missed John. Being a continent away from him and all my family and friends seemed increasingly foolish.

So, after about seven weeks total spent in the jungle, and through an especially doe-eyed conversation on video chat, John and I agreed it was time for me to return. I scheduled my flight for the following week, refusing John's offer to fly down to accompany me, and exhaled a big sigh of relief.

After sharing bittersweet goodbyes with Pablo, the center's staff, and my new friends, Julien and I loaded my stuff and ourselves into the moto-taxi for my final departure. Because my symptoms had progressed since I initially flew down with John, the sixteen-hour solo journey home would prove comically epic, including four rickety airline wheelchairs, shameless staring from onlookers, marathon fumbling sessions with my passport, fights with zippers that I never won, award-worthy performances by my bladder, and one near-miss redo of my head vs. concrete. But the most simple miracle were the kind helpers who managed to shepherd me back to Colorado with my dignity and faith in humanity still largely intact.

Despite the challenges, I felt triumphant as an adventurer, functional body or no. I did it, I took a chance, and gave it my all. I also knew that one of the best parts of traveling is the eventual letting go of travel itself, of returning to the nurturing familiarity of home once home calls. And since I had now left the jungle, I knew I could continue to mine the marvels it had uncovered from the safety of my bug-free, comfort-heavy, honey-loving suburban American home.

11.

Surviving Dislocation

O nce back home with John, we had the kind of sweet, almost shy reunion that comes after a big event neither of us knew how to talk about yet. After tending to my immediate needs of unpacking a few items and beginning to make dinner, we initiated a progressively unfolding discussion on what had happened in Peru, which lasted for at least three days, late into the evenings, first thing in the mornings, and the hours in between, helping us begin to make sense of what had previously felt too big and jumbled to make sense of.

Amidst the reflection, we began looking forward. Because I was in worse physical shape than when we'd left, it was no longer safe or practical to have me sitting at home alone all day. While I could pull prepared food from the fridge in theory, my weak grip afforded me a 50/50 chance of getting it anywhere but the floor, which I could not bend down steadily enough to reach, nor reliably rise from if I fell. So we began considering how to find a daytime caregiver for my highly independent, prideful self. *Gulp.*

Within a few days we found a temporary solution; a young friend from the Lyme community needed a place for herself and her boyfriend to stay while attempting to get settled in the area. She was willing to offer practical help for me around the house while she looked for work, and because she knew chronic illness well, she took sympathy for our difficult situation. Her only requirement was a clean home; after having battled with Lyme carditis for years, she needed a home free of toxins to give her compromised immune system a chance to continue healing. I reassured her that we only used natural and gentle personal and household products, and upon purchase a year prior, the home inspector had been impressed with how well cared for the structure had been. She and her boyfriend arrived with their suitcases a few days later and we spent the afternoon getting to know each other. They were a kind and gracious couple.

The next day, we didn't see or hear from either of them, until I got a call from Tony, the boyfriend, in the late afternoon. He sounded strangely hesitant as he explained what had happened to Becki in the last twenty-four hours.

"I'm so sorry to tell you this. But last night, Becki... she got really... sick."

"Oh no! Is she okay? Sick how?" I asked.

"Well... she kinda collapsed at the grocery store," he said.

"Oh wow, that's awful! How strange! Do you have any idea why?" I asked.

"I'm so sorry to say this, but maybe you have mold in your house? We think so. She only reacts like this in moldy buildings, and we had to leave your house late last night because her arm went paralyzed and her face was numb, and then we went to the grocery store thinking she might get better walking around somewhere else, but she had a seizure there… so… we've been at the emergency room all day." He had a note of defeat in his voice.

"Oh my God… I'm so sorry," I sputtered.

"I hate to say this… but we can't come back. And maybe you should leave that house too? Maybe it's what's making you sick?" he asked.

Oh, shit, I thought. *Here we go.*

———

The warnings about mold had by this time been rolling in for months. Health-savvy friends had been urging me to test our home since living in a moldy environment is a major illness risk factor. But our 1963 split level had had an exceptionally positive inspection before purchase. It wasn't in the flood zone and had no signs of water damage, nor any reports of it. Most importantly, whereas the communal home where I had lived in the past had smelled suspiciously musty long before we knew it was moldy, this one smelled clean. Before entering the endless world of environmental dangers associated with chronic illness, we thought these measures were enough. *Bzzzzt! Wrong.*

So, while I had a stomach lurch at the thought of entering a moldy rabbit hole, I also felt a surge of excitement that maybe we had finally located the cause of my unresponsive symptoms. If only one night in our house could cause a healthier person temporary paralysis, what could living in a succession of moldy homes for years do to me? Could this explain John's tanking health? Furthermore, could this be the "curse"? Perhaps the "dark, malevolent energy" that had reportedly entered our home was just a lethal, man-sized shadow of hidden mycotoxins. It struck both John and me that less than a week after returning from Peru, where shamans had worked on my behalf to lift a "curse," we uncover a literal toxic infestation in our midst—via a highly unlikely series of events, no less.

I called John at work and left a message that started with, "Uh, really bad news which might be kinda good, babe?" In the coming days we did everything we knew to do: ordered an at-home test, scoured the Internet for recommendations about reputable mold inspectors, asked our friends who were familiar with this shadowy reality for advice. Mostly these friends began telling us to get out of the house—ASAP. This was not practical, yet I knew they were probably right; each day breathing in mycotoxins was only going to weaken both of us further, and might mean life or death for my overburdened immune system.

The inspector showed up within a week, confirming the same thing the at-home test did: our home was mega toxic, currently unfit for any human or animal inhabitants. Since he came highly recommended for his long and trustworthy career, it was shocking to hear him add the detail that the numbers his machines recorded were among the worst he'd ever seen. Apparently, faulty sealing in the shower window in our master bath had caused ongoing but hidden water damage for years. He said, "Without someone taking this tub out, I can only guess what that inside wall looks like, although I bet it's a solid wall of thick black mold."

I thought of all the times I had spent in that very tub, taking long "detox" baths, inadvertently filling my lungs with sticky immune-depressing black fungus. *Uh... oops.*

He must have been thinking along the same lines, because he reminded me that he was well versed on toxic mold's effect on the human body. "Do you believe this contamination could cause my severity of neurological symptoms?" I asked. Beholding my atrophied hands, stiff gait, and garbled voice, he slowly nodded. While fighting back tears, he said gently, "If I were you, I'd get out of here as quick as possible."

———

Lucky for us, we weren't the first ones who had been through this. We were friends with a couple who had just emerged through a multi-year mold hell and were finally finding recovery. To our surprise, during a phone call we thought was meant simply for advice, they invited us to stay with them in their newly purchased, verified non-toxic home near downtown Boulder as we figured things out. We gratefully accepted their offer and marveled at our good fortune. Just one important detail though: we couldn't bring anything with us. We had to leave *everything* behind except our IDs, keys, and phones, and even then only after they were carefully cleaned.

After all, our friends knew from our test results that we had had a severe contamination of toxic molds, including the notoriously sticky Stachybotrys. They knew that this toxin can contaminate every porous item in the vicinity, so unless you ditch everything that was in the building also, your chances of staying sick and re-infecting a clean environment with invisible toxins is disturbingly high. So, in fear of contaminating their new house (something we could not do) or our future selves (also something we could not do), we resolved to be as thorough as possible in starting afresh with clean items. In the days leading up to our departure, we sat at our computers—the very computers we were about to leave behind, along with everything else we owned—while swimming in adrenaline and ordering the new items we would need sent to our friends' house for our arrival: a few shirts, one or two pairs of pants, underwear, socks, belt, pajamas, a wallet, a bag, a pair of shoes.

Before our move date, we scrambled to get our home ready. This included giving away our four chickens, by this point barely a year old. I placed an ad on Craigslist offering them to a good home, and a single mom from across town came to pick them up that same evening, cardboard boxes in tow. I didn't bother to tell her what their names or quirky personalities were, and would realize only later that her kids would enjoy naming them themselves. In the moment I was focused on quieting an inner shock.

We tried to prepare for the weeks of unknowns ahead by collecting passwords, medical records, paperwork, passports, and IDs we thought we might need, sealing them in plastic bags and bins and storing in the trunk of my car. We didn't yet have a plan for dealing with the rest of our moldy items once we left; all we knew is we'd lock the doors and windows, let our beloved plants die, and figure out the details once we were more stable—which seemed an impossible likelihood at some unknown moment in the future.

We found a temporary home for Anu with a friend of ours from Denver who he'd be safe with, again trying to ignore the growing hole in my chest as John crated him. He spoke softly,

"It's okay, punkin. We're coming back for you... it's just for a little while. It's okay."

Anu offered scared meows as John handed the heavy crate to our friend. We reminded each other we'd see him again; we just had no idea when.

On move day, we had instructions to pull into our hosts' garage, strip naked, seal our moldy clothes in plastic bags, stuff them in the bottom of their outdoor trash bins, and immediately head for a shower once inside. I had to remind myself that, yes, I could wear my favorite blouse and jeans for the drive over, because all my clothes would ultimately end up in the trash anyway.

As we backed out of our driveway on our way over, we shared a surreal moment of adrenalized escape. We had started our life together in this home, yet that life had taken such an unexpected and drastic turn since we'd moved in that it could hardly be considered the same one. I tried to block out this grief and bewilderment; it was too much to behold. But despite the feelings we had about these big changes, we knew they may precede the return of my health, a gift so precious that we would have given anything for it. We just hoped we had effectively bottomed out on suffering and stepped into our newly promising post-toxic life.

12.
Spinning Heads

I t turned out that "bottoming out" on suffering wasn't quite on the menu yet.

A week after our escape, we found ourselves back in the driveway of our moldy home, having by this point endured a bumpy ride. The friends we had first moved in with had been gracious and accommodating, but five days into our stay, they informed us that our very presence in their home was causing them to relapse into mold illness. Because we had been so careful to arrive clean, they explained this could really only mean the mold fungus had already colonized within one or both of us in infection form—probably me—and we were essentially off-gassing toxins into their new pristine space every time we coughed or even exhaled. I had heard this could happen, and it could explain why I continued to get weaker even away from home. So, despite our mission to shed all our contaminated stuff, we were still stuck with the one thing I couldn't even try to replace: my darn body.

After realizing we could no longer stay with them, we quickly traveled through a succession of homes other friends offered us. During this expedition we realized that one week in a clean environment was all we needed to be able to feel the difference between walking into a toxic home and walking into a safe one. We entered two supposedly clean homes that clearly weren't; I got dizzy headaches within ten minutes of entering. Like Becki and so many others, I was beginning to develop a special sense for mold toxicity.

After the third failed attempt at locating a safe place to stay, we ended up back in the car with our now small amount of worldly possessions in the back seat. For some reason we had decided to drive back to our home across town and park in the driveway, perhaps since it at least felt familiar, even if only in a *Twilight Zone* sort of way. We didn't know where we'd be sleeping; if we slept inside, it would contaminate the only safe clothes we now owned; we could sleep in our backyard, but neither of us wanted to step inside to retrieve moldy blankets and pillows; a motel would be a mold risk like anywhere else, and we couldn't afford it. So there we sat outside our beloved home, repelled from entering by an invisible dark force.

By this point it was about three in the afternoon. We had already emailed and left voicemails with other friends who had offered places to stay. The car felt stuffy. We were hungry and tired. Before long, unsure what else to do, we started sniping at each other.

"Why are you getting sharp with me? I didn't do anything."

"Oh, and I did? Are you saying I shouldn't tell you I'm hungry? Wow, new lows over here."

I contemplated telling John to come over and help me out of my seat so I could slowly hobble away from him and the car, careful not to trip on my own feet. "Oh yeah? Watch this," I would say, inching my sorry body down the driveway without looking back. I decided against this, knowing it wouldn't have the dramatic flourish a fighting exit deserves. And since I was largely dependent on him, he wouldn't allow himself to ditch me in our cramped car while he exercised his adrenaline for a walk. So there we sat, each stuck in our slowly burning resentments, both fully aware of how futile it was to turn our stress on each other.

And then we got the text from a friend from our meditation community: "You guys can stay with us; we'd be happy to host you. Our newly built basement apartment is definitely free of water damage. You can come anytime and enter through the back door."

And with that, whatever petty complaints John and I were harboring toward each other deflated. *YES!* We both sighed some relief, apologized for squabbling, and agreed to find some local comfort food on the way over. One more disaster concluded.

———

The Sunday morning after a week spent in our friend's basement, we found ourselves pulling into the parking lot of a new potential rental situation in an up-and-coming outskirt of town. The apartment complex had looked fancy and modern online, although in person it looked even more corporate than I imagined. As we parked in front of the leasing office, I squelched the urge to yawn theatrically, although I assumed John was thinking the same thing. We already knew the amenities all registered somewhere between irrelevant to eyeroll-inducing: *A tapas bar coffee shop! A dog grooming parlor! Gigantic widescreen TVs in the twenty-four-hour fitness center!*

Nonetheless, I tried to stay positive. We knew this complex was built after the flood which had recently contaminated many homes and buildings in the county, and now housed at least a few mold-sensitive refugees safely. And, to be extra cautious, some friends with mold-sniffing superpowers were meeting us here for the walk through.

Since meeting people who might find themselves falsely cheerful and weird around a disabled person didn't sound fun, I opted to stay in the car during the tour and leasing conversation. At least, it wouldn't be as much fun as undisturbed scrolling through my Facebook ALS groups feed, looking for evidence of how to heal progressive paralysis via mold detox. There was nothing new since the day before: a few research articles, a few vague accounts of partial recoveries, a handful of patients who felt the mold was their primary trigger to illness but whose doctors never took them seriously. At some point I looked up and realized the glum overcast sky matched my mood.

John and our friends returned to the car a half hour later with the update: while the leasing office had synthetic air fresheners strong enough to induce a headache, the ground-floor one-bedroom they saw had passed the sniff test. It was clean. It was wheelchair accessible, should I eventually need that. The light was decent. There was a south-facing patio. It would be available in three days. And… it was nearly twice the cost of our monthly moldy-home mortgage, at only a third of the space. John and I had a thirty-second conversation consisting mostly of:

Dang!

Dang!

Do we have other options?

Not really, huh?

Dang! Okay, let's do it.

And with that, we had a new home.

———

As we moved in days later, we realized how unfun it is to have an apartment without any stuff to fill it with. Our heads began spinning as we tried to figure out which items would be necessities for our immediate functioning, and which could wait; what might be salvageable from our moldy home, and who would salvage it, with what time and energy. And do I really need all these expensive tests and supplements and medications my new mold doctor is recommending? How many towels are necessary to order now? What kind of new hair barrettes are cheap enough but still do the trick? Are we settled enough to get Anu back? What can I get done for John, without having to ask?

Ah, John. Right in front of me, so near, and yet difficult to reach beyond the endless and immediate stresses. After all, John was by now getting tired. In between the tasks of putting the details together in our new life, in between his working full-time and doing all the cooking and cleaning, in between helping me decide what to buy with our dwindling savings, we strung together only small moments of presence and connection. With those moments, we tried to put together the bigger pieces of understanding what we had just escaped. And, most importantly, we realized that John's head-spinning had started in our moldy house, and it was literal, and it was serious.

Of course we had no idea at the old house why, when trying to walk to the bathroom at night—the toxic one—he would feel like he was walking on a ship in storm waters, the vertigo springing on him suddenly and without explanation. Nor did we know that his word jumblings, weird periods of mental blankness, spacial dyslexia, and overwhelming fatigue that would hit fast and hard were not simply signs of stress—although stress didn't help—but of mycotoxin poisoning. So when his fatigue continued despite us having escaped the source, we agreed he needed treatment also for mold toxicity. Even though his disability was invisible compared to mine, how could he keep shouldering me if he also carried debilitating neurological symptoms?

———

Meanwhile, amidst settling into our new home, we agreed to finally attend an ALS clinic in Denver in case they could offer practical support. The meeting with the neurologist went like this:

Doctor: "So help me understand what you're saying. Your house was found to be filled with toxic mold, your husband also started having neurological symptoms while you lived there, you have these blood-test results showing heavy bacterial infection and immune dysfunction, you have signs of a systemic fungal infection, you're bringing five journal articles linking motor neuron disease to fungal and bacterial toxins with case studies showing halting or reversal of symptoms through utilizing the treatments outlined, and you want us to try to follow up?"

Me: "Uh, yes. Please."

Doctor (sighing): "Well, we don't really do that here. Since ALS has no officially agreed upon cause, from a medical standpoint that's all unconventional. These antifungals might be dangerous, and the suggested treatment here wouldn't be covered by insurance since it's not approved for your condition. Sorry about that, but I took an oath to first do no harm... Are you interested in grief counseling though? I'm happy to write you a referral."

Me: *Dear allopathic medicine, (expletive, expletive, expletive).*

Our suspicions about the clinic had been true; it was only designed to cushion one's descent into paralysis and death. Since a hopeless presumption of decline and the refusal to consider or treat underlying factors didn't strike us as an inspiring treatment approach, I had already taken refuge in a Boulder naturopath who specialized in mold illness. And sure enough, within weeks he got back multiple lab results suggesting I was toxic from mold exposure. What's more, testing revealed that I had the HLA gene, which is correlated with a greatly reduced ability to detox mycotoxins or Borrelia infections. Yet again, the protocols he put me on—including fancy prescriptions to sop up the mold—yielded no noticeable results even at high doses. I was willing to go along, knowing it was my best option, until he started quoting well-disputed talking points of the IDSA. Great, another doctor who doesn't believe in Lyme. *This again?*

And so continued the seemingly never-ending hunt for the miracle-working doctor bold enough to put multiple pieces together, a search so many with poorly understood conditions can continue for years. Some friends with chronic illnesses admitted to cobbling together a team of three or more doctors at once, each with their own specialties and intensive protocols. I went to consultations, listened to interviews, called offices, read endless patient reviews, and weighed the value of putting myself on the radar of expensive doctors with three-year waiting lists. And, like for so many, my search was largely futile; I reliably ended up lacking enough trust to put my rapidly withering body (and checking account) into any given provider's hands. The more experienced I became in reading between the lines of slick articulation and marketing of treatment approaches—which never happened to feature actual ALS reversals—the more hopeless I became in finding my medical hero. Against all logic, I was beginning to think I'd have to do the whole thing myself.

———

Meanwhile my friend Rebecca began to help us coordinate how to deal with our household of likely contaminated stuff. Somehow it was established that she wouldn't mind braving our toxic house to help out, so I silently thanked the gods that I had such a thoroughly unfussy, generous friend with ample free time. Her attitude was basically, "Black mold? *Meh, schmold.* I'll wear a mask. I've survived worse." I could have kissed her.

Our conversations over the coming weeks, by phone or when she came over to make me lunch, which was happening on most days, went something like this:

Me: "Do you think we should throw out *all* of our furniture? The mold websites say it's unethical to try to clean and give it to anyone."

Her: "It does seem drastic, especially if people are notified of the risks and still want it. Seems better to let people use it than wasting stuff. But it's up to you."

Me: "Drastic, right? What a financial and environmental nightmare! But then I read somewhere that even the Old Testament commanded moldy items to be burned."

Her: "Didn't the Bible also say that women were the property of their husbands? I don't know that we need to take all that shit literally."

Me: "Good point. This is impossible! No one should ever be expected to balance all these confusing factors. As a Libra this is the definition of hell…"

Her: "Total hell."

Me: "Let's just… at least… throw out all the bedding for now. First thing's first."

Her: "Yeppers. Done… and hey. Impossible decisions to make with limited information? Life."

Me: "Yeah, well… Life, schmife. I'm kinda over it."

And so it went for months, decision by excruciating decision, until our house was empty enough to remediate and sell, and all our stuff was gone.

———

As anyone who has lost nearly all their possessions in short order knows, it's shocking and hard to make sense of. There are the practical items which you take for granted until they're suddenly missing when you need them—the scissors, the silverware, your rain jacket or purse or pajamas. While the practical items were difficult to lose because suddenly the most basic tasks become impractical, their absence also offered reminders of how disrupted from normalcy life has become: *Wait, how is it I no longer own a single book? And what happened to my house with that nice backyard again?*

This felt especially bewildering since these items—including our beloved house itself—still *appeared* fine and usable; I had to remind myself repeatedly that just because I can't physically see the danger didn't mean it doesn't exist. It was as if a high-risk virus sat more or less on and in each item or surface, was immune to fail-proof cleaning, and since both John and I were immunocompromised, the stakes were too high to risk contact.

But the most difficult items to lose, I found, were made difficult by virtue of them referencing a special relationship or era. The sentimental stuff is what hurt the most: the treasured old photos, the unique furniture, the family quilt that has nursed innumerable illnesses back to health; the poetry from ex-boyfriends, the art, the perfectly broken-in leather boots. I suddenly lost the books that had informed my career, and the journals chronicling decades of changing life. I imagine this is why losing our beloved stuff is a helpful junior-league practice for death, the most complete loss of identity and attachment that we'll all go through eventually.

While this grief of loss was real and would continue to arise in waves, it was nuanced. To my surprise, losing a ton of possessions was *also* partly freeing. Turns out I had been storing unexamined allegiances, past relationship pain, life confusion, and self-doubt with my stuff, being weighed down by old parts of my identity without knowing it. Eventually I realized that I didn't need as much stuff as I had, and John and I were finally able to admit the suburban home and yard and garages and closets of stuff, while luxurious, were more than we wanted or needed responsibility for. Our new, small, one-level one-bedroom felt more reasonable, pristine, and easy to keep organized. Strangely, as painful and costly as our mold tsunami was, it had also served to wipe our eyes clean to see what was truly necessary—and what wasn't.

But though we had been handed a new, lightened perspective in recent months, it didn't mean we both weren't still reeling. Emotionally, mentally, and physically, we had effectively been dislocated, first by my health and prognosis, then John's health, and then from the familiar context and setting for our life together. While we could make peace with losing stuff and losing our location, losing a planned-for future of decades of growth and adventure and companionship together was much harder to swallow. And as we settled into our new apartment, the summer of 2017 turning toward fall, we realized how much our internal compasses were still spinning without steadying anchors in sight.

13.
The Unbearable Intolerability of Receiving Help

FALL 2017

As my illness progressed, so too did my reliance on others. At first it was just John helping make my meals, get my shoes on, open my mail. I could accept his help; he was unembarrassed about offering it. He effectively became my hands and learned how to wash, comb, and style my hair. He gently applied my face wash in the shower as I leaned against the wall. He learned how to assess the virtues of different bras and menstrual products, and learned the difference between tweezing and waxing what, where. On a weekend when both of his sisters were visiting from Illinois, I told them about his rigorous training in caring for me.

He admitted sympathetically, "Yeah, doing 'woman' is seriously no joke," to which they both erupted in satisfied laughter.

But his help had its limits, especially for the nine hours he spent at work each weekday. By this point I was very unsteady on my feet, could barely hold even a plastic dish, could not pour myself a glass of water, and due to weakening muscles in my throat and mouth, could not swallow the loads of supplements I was taking without having someone crush or pour them into liquid. My voice was weak and garbled enough that others had to be listening closely and patiently to understand my comments and questions; phone calls barely worked.

And so we found Ellen through a card tacked to a message board at my doctor's office. Upon first meeting her, I liked that she was mature in age and experience, had a thoughtful manner, and showed a sincere desire to try to make our lives easier. She started coming for four hours on weekdays to make my lunches, help ensure there were always leftover veggie dishes in the fridge, make calls, drive me to appointments. For a couple months it seemed a good-enough fit, and I felt triumphant that I could accept help like an adult. Yet before long, glitches arose, as they have a crafty way of doing in relationships once the honeymoon has faded. It became increasingly clear Ellen moved unbearably slowly and methodically, requiring ample guidance and reassurance each step of the way. Things felt so awkward that Anu disappeared while she was in the house, and only returned from his hidey holes thirty seconds after she'd left and the overall anxiety in the air had plummeted. I wished she knew intuitively how to do things the *right* way (i.e. my way, of course), because I'm such an adult. But with time I began to suspect that whether or not I could somehow mold Ellen into a clone of my former capable and efficient self, she was not—and would never actually be—the true problem. What she *represented* was the bigger problem. Her very presence in our apartment served as a constant, embarrassing reminder that I needed help with even the most basic tasks. So, just like the other new people who entered my sphere only because of the illness but weren't offering hope of recovery—the ALS Association representative telling me about equipment I would someday need, the speech therapists training me how to communicate with my eyes instead of my voice, the social workers urging me to complete my will and medical wishes—I found a good excuse to keep her at arm's length. These people represented impotence and death, arenas I still wasn't fully sold on. It would simply take more time in my role as an adult with a progressive disability for the layers of resistance to wear down enough for me to accept help gracefully.

After agreeing with Ellen it wasn't a great fit after four or five months, we traveled through a succession of other assistants whose tenure with us varied wildly. There was the young woman from Alabama who politely took on more and more responsibility until suddenly announcing an impending five-week trip to India with the expectation my mom could cover for her (nine months); the strong and funny anarchist with ripe body odor who balked at even the gentlest feedback (four months); the uber-efficient and skilled cook who had raised six children but who wound up verbally attacking the other caregivers over how they washed the lettuce (four months). There was the downhome, relaxed, Earth-mama type we liked who surprised us with an unexpected move across the state once fully trained (three months), and the one who told me my bad-vibing energy had been "visiting" her in her meditations prior to her first day of work (a day which ended up lasting a total of forty minutes before I politely informed her it wasn't a fit; she argued viciously on her way out the door).

In the meantime, John stood firmly in my corner anytime I needed to vent about an unfortunate interaction. After returning from work, one of his favorite ways to manage his own anxiety was to fully rearrange the contents of the refrigerator from whatever state the caregiver had left it in. This was the perfect time to assess, on a daily basis, exactly how they were doing. Before long, our geeky therapist gossip would tumble forth shamelessly in detailed discussions on the psychological *role* of health providers overall. We could agree that those who find themselves working as professional helpers are a motley crew. There are those gems who can take responsibility for their own complex motives and feelings about the role, have somewhat flexible yet ultimately intact boundaries, and hold a nice balance of professional tact and efficiency with basic relatability. Further down the scale of helpfulness were those with covert aggression, or who seem to have stickier motives around the themes of being needed, "good," etc., which can signal their own unconscious desires to be taken care of. We agreed that no one needing care should be faced with this kind of transaction—whether or not they have the tools to articulate it. In other words, we got a tad righteous, and enjoyed it.

Eventually, we found Chris. Chris would end up being the best fit John and I could hope for, one of those rare gems on the top of our self-designed scale of helpfulness, smart and quick and can-do. Having already cared for someone with neurological disease for years, she wasn't afraid of my illness in either practical or emotional terms. Deal with random expressions of overwhelming grief? "No biggie." Deal with my likelihood of choking? "Heck, cough that mouthful across the room for all I care." Deal with clueless Medicare representatives by phone? "No problem, I know how to navigate this system." She respected my exacting Goldilocks tendencies and took feedback in stride. But perhaps most important to John and me, her unique tics were on full display from day one—no surprises—and her justice-minded politics and raunchy humor rendered her trustworthy enough to relax around nearly immediately. An Earth angel.

———

Of course, amidst this parade of caregivers, John and I also had our moments of tension—and ours came on a near daily basis. He'd be stumbling through some caregiving task as best he could and I'd think, *Why do I need to explain how to properly place a hair barrette without smushing my hair? Why would he think I want all this bland-ass broccoli—is he mad at me? What is he trying to tell me by giving me this huge glob of toothpaste?*

Because we were still a married couple playing the no-winners "why-would-you-do-it-that-way" game *on top* of my debilitation and his mold-related cognitive dysfunction, we both had plenty of opportunities to polish our styles of reactivity and to practice patience. Turns out it's helpful to express appreciation when things are going well—using actual words, *out loud.* People are basically hyper-verbal houseplants with legs, and they also perk up when regularly adored in simple ways. Or at least my husband is. *Who knew?*

But it's worth noting: I am not an easygoing person, despite a dogged tendency to meditate and an above-average exposure to self-help books. For context: that person who audibly snorts disapproval at the trainee holding up the line at the store checkout? *Yup.* Calls with customer-service representatives which leave both parties in a worse mood, as if being put on hold and transferred kicks up some kind of primal, desperate indignation? *Here.* Yelling at a slow driver? *You'll make me late to my yoga class, dammit!* I even had enough white-woman privilege to show off these entitled habits fearlessly, in public. Which is why getting an illness which requires me and everyone around me to slow down and take stock qualifies as the most unbearable inconvenience, and the most ingenious teacher. It turns the practices of patience, courtesy, and humility into no-joke spiritual disciplines.

Over time and thanks to the co-regulation of John and others trying in earnest to help, my inner pace and rhythm slowly transformed, leaving me softer, tolerating the actions of others with more grace, and tolerating my own vulnerability with more matter-of-factness and humor. It increasingly dawned on me that even though I was becoming increasingly physically dependent, I still had choices; I could make sure everyone was aware of important details before things felt critical; I could remember to breathe, especially if no one was reminding me to; I could choose whether to care so much about how things were done, that maybe it wasn't a big deal if my hair was parted differently than I liked, or if Person A didn't put my sweater on as gracefully as Person B. Maybe, moment by moment, I could learn how to swallow my pride through getting help with the most intimate of tasks, trusting those helping me were mature enough to recognize the vulnerability it required on my part, and perhaps theirs. In this way, I was getting the ongoing opportunity to trust my basic needs would be met, and relax into that space between having a life-affirming desire and its eventual fulfillment. This gradually became a practice of responding with gentleness to every mishap, inconvenience, and disappointment—including the most rank hairstyles.

———

Meanwhile, financial and logistical support for us started coming through on a new level: friends and family donated generously; other friends made a sweet short film of us in an attempt to share our story online and garner more donations; we had a meal train and a care team who held biweekly calls with John to try to organize our growing needs for help.

Even though I knew some of my most wholesome moments of satisfaction came from offering donations to worthy causes or giving my time to a friend in need, when I was the one receiving help, my inner capitalist suddenly balked. *Surely they have better things to do with their resources. Why am I to think we deserve all this attention and care? What are they getting out of it?*

When I confessed these guilt-laden thoughts to friends, I was met with exaggerated eyerolls and reminders: "Teri, you are loved. Deal. What the heck do you think money is for anyway? Trust me, you're worth it." It would take many reassurances to believe that gracefully receiving others' generosity was actually a form of service, in that it provides an opportunity to shed small mindedness, fear, or self-interests. Giving affirms the truth of our connectedness with others, our shared vulnerabilities, our basic love; receiving facilitates giving to take place.

Nonetheless I knew my condition placed a burden of time and money and responsibility on those who chose to show up, since the act of tending to someone with a debilitated body is intimate and demanding, requiring a lot of patience and perseverance. Yet despite this challenge or perhaps because of it, I knew others are presented the ongoing opportunity to slow down, to empathize, to express thoughtfulness on the spot. They are asked to stretch the edges of their own tolerance and generosity, hopefully growing in humility and maturity along the way. In this sense I knew I was in the diamond cave, getting pressurized right along with whoever was helping me, and I could feel fortunate to get to surround myself with those willing enough to also step into the heat of transformation: the most effective meditation retreat none of us ever imagined being on.

14.
Blessed Perspective

FALL 2017

And then there are times when, in the life of a sick person, patience and perspective is entirely too much to ask. After the seventeenth person recommended the *Medical Medium* in hopes my illness might be cured with enough wild blueberries and cilantro tincture, and the fifth person suggested Wim Hof breathing and regularly dunking myself in ice water, I began to scream a little inside with every innovative miracle solution offered to me. And it seemed everyone and their stepsister had one.

But once a new friend told me I sounded "negative" about the challenges of having ALS, and all I needed to do was "think differently" in order to heal, it took everything I had to not tell her where to shove her highly recommended Dynamic Neural Retraining System DVDs. Yes, even though she knew *exactly* what

I was going through since she also had Lyme, and her fatigue was so bad it had even cramped her post-work rock-climbing hobby.

These suggestions were well intentioned, I knew; people just wanted me to survive. Some ideas even retained a certain palliative merit. But after eighteen months of battling illness and having already explored (nearly) every alternative cure possible, I decided I had had quite enough unsolicited health advice. So, like any self-respecting competitive introvert with a passive-aggressive urge, I took my education campaign to Facebook:

Friend, I'm really happy that you've found the magical cure to all illness, and it consists of a celery juice fast while plunging yourself into ice every morning and finally breathing like a real man. I know you think that if I, too, consume acerola-spiked gummy bears before my meals and listen to music only in the 532-megahertz frequency while chanting the original name of God, a prompt and total healing is in order. I do understand that it shortened your cold by two days and improved your dog's hearing within a week. I understand that if I only believed it with enough conviction, it would work for me, too. And no, I won't forget what your cousin Jim learned on his last kombucha cleanse, and how I'll probably learn the same thing, if I make sure to get the right flavor.

You see, I'm not ignoring your advice because it's ridiculous to compare your occasional experience of brain fog to my life-threatening illness. Nor am I insulted by you thinking that what you learned from that sixty-second soundbite on Lyme disease qualifies you to think you now have the answer to this layered, complex illness that I've been researching full-time for years now. It's not any of those reasons that cause me to snicker inside from your well-meaning advice. It's because I tried all that already.

So for now, though it might not make any sense, I'm only taking health advice from my sickest friends. No, not the ones whose occasional tummy aches really cramp their hot yoga practice, but the ones who understand that even determination and fierce grit and critical-thinking skills and open mindedness and endless research and good vibes and clean karma and the smartest free-est-rangeist supplements aren't always enough because if so, we would've kicked this shit by now.

If you've stared down a life-threatening illness this wicked and won, or are fighting with me, bring on the platypus elixir. I'm all ears. If instead you cured your athlete's foot with high dose intranasal vitamin K and you intuitively know it'll work for me too, do us both a favor and just tell me you're thinking of me.

Oh, and one more thing: There's no S in Lyme.

If emojis had volume, my sickest friends cheered the loudest. Nonetheless I wound up disappointed that no one sent me treatment ideas for months after that.

A few months into settling into our new apartment, we invited dear friends Jamie and Sophia over for dinner. After sitting down for buffalo chili and kale salad, we soon began updating each other on recent events. John and I shared about the bee venom therapy, our newest Lyme treatment venture. "Ten live bees down my spine each time, three times a week. People doing it say it doesn't hurt. They lie," I said, with John translating my slurred words so our friends could understand. "That shit hurts." We shared how our own vibrant beehive behind our moldy house had recently been ransacked by wasps; another small but not insignificant loss. John discussed the agonizingly slow improvement he was seeing from the mold treatment he'd started, and how I, unfortunately, wasn't having any improvements.

"That would be too easy, huh? We apparently need more challenge," John said, which we all cackled at.

Soon the conversation turned to them. We already knew that they had been having a hard time as a couple, especially with supporting their teenager struggling in addiction treatment. We soon learned that they were experiencing simultaneous crises in paying for his treatment, to the extent that they were temporarily homeless and living out of vehicles, Sophia had been demoted due to a new disability after an injury, and due to the stress they had struggled to relate to each other at all at some points, questioning if their relationship could survive. This left John and I staring at them, wondering how they were functioning at all, let alone making it over for a dinner date with us. But before any of us knew it, five hours went by, most of it being spent in raucous, table-slapping laughter about how absurd all our lives had become after being so stable just a few years prior.

John exclaimed, "You guys really don't need to compete with us for who can endure a more drastic, Book-of-Job-type life. We knew you were competitive, but *really*."

Sophia agreed: "Well, someone needed to give you a run for your money."

The dialogue might have grown slightly maniacal, despite the calming croon of Lou Reed in the background.

Collectively, we were tapping into how good it can feel to have our dark bubbles pierced by others who are intimate with heartbreak. And we all get to start somewhere in relating creatively to our losses, even if it's only in cursing: "A hundred names for God? I'll give you my hundred names for God." I already knew falling into the underworld had cracked something open for me, eventually allowing more life, juice, and movement to flow into areas within my psyche which used to be dry, heavy, shut down. The bullshit sloughed off; the unbending rules of seriousness were no longer so necessary or helpful, if indeed they ever were. The important things got more important, and everything else became fair game for satire. And apparently I wasn't alone in this.

Our other friends whose lives were going according to plan were usually less fun to have over. Our visits with them often felt somber, as if they felt pressure to respect the gravity of our situation with a mixture of reverence and humble guilt at how well their own lives were unfolding in comparison. They were not unwise; whenever someone is surviving a mighty ordeal, it's safer to let them take the lead of setting the ratio of gravity to levity. Nevertheless, this put John and I in the unique position of wanting to cheer our visitors up a bit. "There there, life's not so bad! It's okay to laugh a little. After all, we're all together on this sinking ship of ego. You're next!… Haha, just kidding, kinda…"

Adding to our spectacle—and the need to let go of sense-making—was my pseudobulbar affect, which causes those of us with certain neurological conditions to emote strangely. Since it's only minimally related to actual emotion, it's mind-twisting to behold. While some people are easily triggered to crying, for some merciful reason, my version consistently tilted toward uncontrollable laughter and smiling. This meant I'd end up seeming amused at those moments when you're supposed to show concern that, say, your husband just banged his head on the cabinet, or your friend tells you her mom just got hit by a bus. "Hahahaha! Haha! Ha," I'd giggle and beam for minutes, approaching the sensitivity level of a schoolyard bully.

No matter how often I tried to explain this emotional incontinence to others, they could rarely confidently discern between my true delight and anxious agitation. They'd usually wind up surprised by how hard and long I'd laugh at the completely unfunny things they were saying or doing, sometimes rolling with it by creating jokes. Which by itself was decidedly funny and would cause me to laugh in earnest.

But it was usually later, when John and I were alone, that we'd feel free to really let it rip. Lucky for me, John is funny. When I first met him I found his humor odd and impossibly goofy at times, in peculiar contrast to my bone-dry approach. But here, many years later and softened by the losses we carried, we trusted ourselves and each other to play more. When I'd spill my whole cup of water down my front due to spastic arm tremors before breakfast, John would reply in exasperation, "Babe, I told you the wet T-shirt contest wasn't until tonight! Too early!" Or, after seeing the fascinating wormy results of my successful parasite cleanse, he would announce with a celebrity voice, "Ladies and gentlemen, I present to you... the hostess with the leastess!" then demand with a stern British accent, "Everybody out of the pool!" In those moments we became more than a couple bearing an unbearable situation; we were reclaiming the delightful absurdity of life itself.

———

Always wanting more perspective on the soul journey, and with plenty of time to read while John was at work, I discovered some books making the case for pre-birth planning. The authors of these books shared anecdotal reports from hypnotic regression of the between-lives state, arguing how as souls desiring spiritual growth above all else, we agree before incarnation to have certain challenges, circumstances, and relationships helping us toward our goals.

Before long, John and I began voicing the planning session we must have had as pre-incarnate souls:

Teri: I'm feeling ambitious.

John: Uh-oh.

Teri: Yeah. I'm sick of these easy lives we've been having of plague and famine. Yawn! Let's really go for it this time.

John: Hmm. I know what most of those other souls are planning right now. [In a mocking voice] "Let's throw in one or two moderate, common challenges, just enough to grow a little." Lightweights.

Teri: I told you that you had to stop making fun of the Slow Path beings! But, yeah, between you and me, *suckaz!*

John: So… how hard should we make it?

Teri: Like, *so* hard.

John: Should we throw in any especially impossible tidbits?

Teri: Totes. How about I get paralyzed right after you've married me? And we discover black mold all over everything we own? Let's go all out.

John: Whoa… Yeah… Wicked.

Teri: Do you think it's over the top if I start drooling at some point due to the illness?

John: No, that's perfect. I'll finally learn to multitask. Maybe you should even have uncontrollable snot when you're crying which I'll have to deal with. Let's make you so paralyzed that you can't even blow your own nose… even when we're *fighting*.

Teri: No! You think? You really are a sadist *and* a masochist, aren't you? Don't forget that Trump looks likely to be president around that time too. Aren't we going too far?

John [chuckling]: Probably. But you started it.

Teri: You know we'll take it seriously right? What with the whole forgetting thing.

John: We always do.

Teri: At least once it's over and we're doing the post-life debrief, we'll have a riot reminiscing.

John: Yeah. And we'll be mega evolved compared to now.

Teri: OMG, L-O-V-E how you think, you sassy soulmate you! I know I'll majorly regret this while we're in the thick of it, but I'm in. Let's do this wacko human thing!

Fist bump light as air, our guides share looks of concern.

John: Haha! Watch out little innocent "John" and "Teri"! Bombs away!

15.
The Wisdom
to Know the Difference

As I settled into the simple routine in our tiny apartment, in between the bee-stinging therapy and the wayward colonics appointment, I was afforded the time to reflect on how I was, and was not, working with my mind. There seemed to be roadblocks everywhere. Therapy was hard without much of a voice; I couldn't easily attend meetings in church basements; even venting in emails to sympathetic friends was getting more difficult because the remaining strength in my thumbs—the best way to type on my phone—took more energy to exercise than it was worth.

And meditation was complicated with baggage.

It started at twenty-four, when I had found myself in a Theravadin Buddhist monastery in Northern Thailand after a hasty escape from India. Though I had planned on backpacking and teaching English alone through Western India for six months, by three months I was thoroughly rattled, disturbed, and left with boogers so black that a meditation retreat in a quieter nearby country was the only thing that made sense. Never mind that I had never before meditated. I spent a large portion of the three-week retreat trying to sort out why I tortured myself with impossible ventures, what had happened in India, and what I was trying to accomplish by sitting on the floor for hours with an aching butt and closed eyes, pretending not to think.

But as the weeks wore on sitting in the nearly empty shrine room, sensing the sweet incense slowly curling designs into the stillness beyond my busy mind, something tight and hurting inside began to gently unravel. By the time my retreat was coming to a close, I could agree with the head teacher in residence that meditation did, in fact, hold something of value for me, all difficulty with the practice aside. Even though following my breath for hours didn't take away my twenty-something loneliness or self-aggression, it allowed me new glimpses of calm, and even a basic contentment previously unfamiliar to my ever-seeking self. It was as if the years of low-grade panic and mental clutter collected thus far were finally allowed to off-gas into the quiet, still space around my body, affording me the long-avoided yet nourishing space to just feel, and to just be.

By the time I started my graduate program in Contemplative Psychotherapy the following year at Naropa—a "Buddhist inspired" university in Boulder, which led me to Reggie—mindfulness meditation had become as much a staple of my daily routine as brushing my teeth or washing my face: I just did it, trying to not overthink the outcome. While placing my attention on my breath was often-times relaxing, sometimes anesthetizing, and occasionally straight up torturous, I knew the payoff was well worth the time I gave it each morning. Over time, the practice helped strengthen my witnessing awareness of my thoughts and behaviors, both helpful and unhelpful, and generally chip away at my judgments of myself and others. Due to the hours on the cushion adding up over the next decade of daily practice, staying put through the highs and lows, eventually it became easier to trust the workability of situations, no matter how bleak they appeared on first glance.

But fast-forward to the day after diagnosis, I walked past my shrine area of our bedroom with a confused revulsion. In the process of doing Ngöndro with all its goals and milestones, under Reggie's tutelage, something had changed for me. I suddenly recognized how hard I'd been pushing to do this ambitious meditative *thing* to get somewhere I thought I needed to be—somewhere more evolved, somewhere spiritually "better." Yet if the new state of my life were any indication, it hadn't quite paid off. I was spiritually fatigued.

John and I attended one more advanced retreat with him a few months later, to see if I could continue to relate to my meditation cushion in a useful way. On some level, I knew it would have been useful just to sit for hours and let my ongoing fear and discursive scheming gently wear down and soften me. Instead, I spent most of that time lying on the ground, my cushion as a pillow, trying to relax into the feeling someone had shot a fucking cannon into my lower belly.

But even months before I attended this final retreat, things were feeling increasingly weird with Reggie and leadership. A number of friends had been quietly leaving the sangha for years, unable to reconcile his teachings on compassion, equanimity, and non-judgment with his own increasingly paranoid and hostile behavior. Reggie would take opportunities to publicly attack the character, devotion, or practice of students who left, saying things like, "They didn't have what it takes," a narrative which never quite added up. In my year spent as his assistant, he had sometimes asked me to help him do damage control by reaching out kindly to students he'd recently attacked. When I'd oh-so-gently suggest he could be more patient or listen more, he'd say I brought too much of a "therapist lens" to how people should be treated; "The Vajrayana is different." In an attempt to honor my teacher—something I had vowed to do—and remain a part of the community I loved, I tried to quell my internal dissonance and go along. I thought that with enough time and attention to skillful feedback from students, he would surely change. For some reason I believed he wanted to.

But emboldened by the #MeToo movement and increasing exposures of abusive Buddhist and spiritual teachers, more and more people outside the sangha seemed to openly question the true sanity of the "crazy wisdom" lineage. Reggie's guru Trungpa Rinpoche was widely known as an alcoholic who got away with all kinds of behavior that would be recognized as sexually, physically, and emotionally abusive in non-Vajrayana contexts, a number of his heirs followed suit in various ways, and rumors of a culture of abuse in our bigger sister sangha Shambhala were growing stronger by the month.

So by the time Reggie urged us all to take another new, more explicit vow of devotion toward him as the guru—a request he made just before my diagnosis—I snorted in refusal. I knew the *person* of the teacher wasn't supposed to be the object of devotion as much as *the principle of awakening* the guru represents; yet my teacher's character was becoming increasingly unhinged. Something was off, even though I didn't yet fully understand what to make of it.

After leaving my last retreat with Reggie, I didn't formally meditate for a year. I couldn't—and didn't care to try. Once I found myself in Peru, even the instructions to sit upright "like a warrior," for hours in ceremony felt too punishing and harsh, holding a masculine overlay which didn't fit my situation. Been there, done that, and now suspected warriorship was overrated. Giving myself permission to lay my weakened body back on the mattress after drinking ayahuasca felt kind. And kindness felt healing.

It was at the first center that Keyo had plopped some books in front of me by authors he thought I would like. Of them, Dr. Joe Dispenza's *You Are the Placebo* caught my attention the most. Dispenza shared his own story of an improbable healing after a paralyzing accident by visualizing his spinal cord reknitting itself for hours on end over many weeks lying in bed.

In the following week of the retreat I'd lie on my own grungy bed in the relentless humidity, reading through his meditations and wondering if I could find the discipline to give them the consistent attention they would require. His method made some sense, though I was not ready to jump in without a committed and convincing plan for doing so. And once I left the center and the book behind, my enthusiasm slowly faded into the background as I continued to focus my attention on physical treatments.

But now back home from Peru over a year later, having exhausted even more treatment attempts to no avail, I felt discouraged. Whereas my previous training taught me to be wary of any meditation or mind training which attempts to manufacture reality according to our liking—because, according to Buddhist philosophy, the far more reliable vehicle for unconditional fulfillment within the roller coaster known as human existence is through accepting impermanence and imperfection—I still couldn't accept my prognosis. Equanimity could go to hell where ALS was concerned. So when I stumbled across a random email advertising Dispenza's video teachings on radical belief changing, remembering how I liked his book, I was more ready to give his ideas serious consideration. I didn't even mind that it might vindicate Gabriella and my uppity rock-climbing friend.

"Dr. Joe," as he was affectionately called by students, was in a decidedly different camp than the Buddhist peace-touting gurus who strove for mere equanimity and wisdom. Not content with ordinary reality and its fickle, intermittent payoffs, he encouraged his students to go "quantum," to manifest whatever they could imagine, to become "supernatural"; mostly, to reject the narrative of limitation and lack of control over their destinies. Though he was actually a chiropractor and not the neuroscientist some online sources assert he is—he would need actual credentials for that—I was willing to suspend judgment; he was, after all, pulling together different lines of research to assert his case. And though this is the kind of thing my sober-minded Buddhist friends would laugh at, by now I had effectively ejected myself from the path of belief and teacher I had once chosen. I was therefore free to drop any ideas about the right way to work with the mind and be a beginner again. Plus, I didn't have to tell anyone.

In his videos, Dr. Joe kept outlining arguments for how our habitual thoughts lead to our habitual emotions, which builds our personality, which affects our genetic expression and immune system—and, most importantly, we can systematically reconstruct these neural networks through consistent effort. So far, I found all of this plausible; kind of an amped up cognitive behavioral therapy, and in some ways similar to Ngöndro, sans Buddhist dogma. Most notably, he outlined a step-by-step strategy for actually doing it, a practical detail most metaphysical proponents were vague on.

Over the next two months, I watched Dr. Joe's lectures daily and began practicing his meditations. John would set me up on the futon before leaving for work, which would give me a good two hours alone before my caregiver arrived. I'd lean back, put my feet on the walker, shut my eyes, and follow along with Dr. Joe as he taught me how to shift my beliefs.

Whereas I had before been carrying the belief, "physical healing is unlikely," now I would practice the feeling of "healing is natural," or "I am already healed," allowing myself to fully inhabit this alternative idea. Through this process, I'd picture myself living as if it was true: jogging up a trail again in the rocky foothills, the wind whipping my hair, gratitude in my total physical recovery overflowing. Sometimes I'd imagine myself on stage somewhere, telling my story of healing through a microphone with a clear voice. By the end of the hour-long meditations I'd often have tears of gratitude streaming down my face because the act of imagination was so thoroughly convincing and exhilarating. When this was coupled with Joe's lectures on how this practice builds new synaptic connections in the brain due to neuroplasticity, I felt I had found an important inner key to support my ongoing physical treatments.

Over the subsequent weeks and months of continuing these meditations, it seemed increasingly clear that despair was still optional. But this felt different than bypassing; I felt that even if the meditations didn't noticeably affect my physical health, they were worth doing for my quality of life. After all, I was transforming my mindset to one more practiced in gratitude, possibility, and worthiness to receive, which could never hurt. Even if humans don't "create" our objective realities, I knew how we can create (or at least heavily influence) our *subjective* realities through our outlooks. So I was reminded of the beauty of Reinhold Niebuhr's Serenity Prayer, as often shared at the end of twelve-step meetings: "God, grant me the serenity to accept the things I cannot change, courage to change the things I can, and wisdom to know the difference."

16.
An Adventure
of Vulnerability

WINTER 2018

Throughout the summer and fall of 2018 I continued to practice the new meditations. I also watched Dr. Joe's lectures regularly, absorbing his understanding of the science behind the mind/body connection. Dr. Joe had been inviting researchers and scientists to his week-long retreats to measure brain activity, heart-rate variability, and electrical activity of his students in meditation over the course of the retreats, and they reportedly found significant physiological shifts within many, including with some who had significant neurological conditions like multiple sclerosis and Parkinson's. A number of them found their symptoms subsiding over the course of his retreat and the weeks and months after;

some of these cases of improbable improvement were documented by test scores and lab markers.

So I began scheming. Dr. Joe's website advertised an upcoming retreat in Cancun in December 2018, at that point just two months away. I met the criteria for a scholarship, had enough free flight miles, and knew John could use FMLA leave as my caregiver since it was a "medical" trip in a certain highly liberal sense. I figured that even if it didn't help my body, at least we'd get another adventure which would give our goodbye some class and comfort—one more "one last adventure" after the previous year's "one last adventure" to Peru, except this one would be more glam. Who couldn't benefit from a little end-of-life celebration with their beloved while sharing tropical drinks on a Caribbean beach anyway?

The one glaring challenge was how utterly impractical a trip would actually be. By now I could barely feed myself, stand, hold a water bottle, speak in anything but the most garbled and soft voice, or use the bathroom alone. It would require even more attention and energy from John than any of our previous adventures. But the idea made me buzz with excitement nonetheless, so I figured it made sense to at least feel out his response.

Knowing John operates best with radical ideas when approached slowly, I got methodical. For a few nights, I'd play Dr. Joe's best lectures in the living room while John was making dinner, turning it just loud enough for him to hear over the clanging dishes and bubbling food on the stove. Within another few days, I casually started saying, "Hey, watch this for ten minutes with me, will ya?", hoping he'd build interest. Luckily, John had also read Dr. Joe's *Placebo*, and had been noticing my mood gradually improve since I'd started the daily meditations. Before long, my little plan paid off, with John agreeing nearly immediately to my wild proposal and even reminding me, "We said we would try anything, right?" I would have clapped and squealed if I could have; instead, he got my googly eyes and big grin. In the following days, he requested time off work, I arranged for Anu to take a vacation at a friend's, and we started shopping for affordable bathing suits online.

———

Once we arrived in balmy Cancun two months later—a welcome change from our Colorado December—it was clear that the airport and transport vehicles were not built with someone like me in mind.

"Where the hell are the ramps in the sidewalk?" John asked while navigating the crowded arrivals area outside, clearly annoyed.

After wheeling me around for twenty minutes in search of the vehicle scheduled to take us to the hotel, we realized it was the huge, school-bus-style one with the steep steps.

The retreat coordinator standing in front with a clipboard frowned at me and said to John, "She'll just have to walk on board and we'll have a seat in the front. Just a few steps she can do, yes?"

I gave John my there's-no-way-don't-even-ask look and shook my head. His protectiveness was then turned roughly on the coordinator: "No, this won't work. You need to send another vehicle, now. We were told there would be disability accommodations, so *accommodate*."

I cringed, noting how I would have handled it more gently if I had a voice—but I didn't. All I had to do, I reminded myself, was sit there and trust everyone to handle everything in the best way they saw fit.

But we weren't alone with our special needs. When our small van arrived half an hour later, a handful of plus-sized or ability-challenged participants were waiting to amble on board. Once John got our luggage in, he came back to me sitting outside the vehicle shaking my head, signifying I would not even be able to navigate the one step up the threshold to the van floor, steadying arms be damned. Because his back was tweaked from transferring me many times a day for many months, and since we couldn't afford him being injured further, he asked the driver to help. I sighed; the driver sighed; John nodded us on. So I surrendered to my own helplessness and let the awkward act be done.

When we arrived at the center a half hour later, once again I was lifted completely by the concierge men waiting to tend to each arriving vehicle, this time two at a time. They pulled me up from the van seat with arms under my legs and back, walked in tandem up a couple steps, and gently placed me in my wheelchair, making sure I felt satisfied with how I landed. After I nodded and smiled, they flashed relieved grins, proud of their good work.

And thus began the parade of unfamiliar men picking up my floppy body and hoisting me in or out of a vehicle many times daily. When I learned to relax, I'd realize it wasn't so bad, and I was humbled by gratitude at their help. Some of them would even be cute, or smell good, or—jackpot—*both*. I came away from these encounters knowing who used hair product or drank coffee or liked spicy food; I observed who was insecure in their strength or spatial reasoning, who didn't take suggestions well from others, and who hesitated when figuring out the mechanics of transferring me safely. Perhaps most importantly, I noted that just because I was the physically weak one, the disclosures and vulnerability were in some ways shared during such an intimate moment between strangers.

———

The first lecture with Dr. Joe was the evening after our arrival. After wheeling me into the crowded ballroom filled with 900 buzzing, giddy people waiting for the introductory talk, some sitting shyly, some dancing to the blaring pop music, we found our team leader, who was anticipating our arrival. He greeted us warmly and showed us the spots he'd saved for us by the aisle.

I took note of the others in our section, curious who we'd be getting to know in the coming week. The woman sitting in the seat next to my wheelchair stuck her hand out to shake mine, flashing a big smile as she introduced herself. I nodded and smiled, knowing there was no way for her to understand my voice in the crowd. I lifted my curled, limp hand so she could grab hold if she still chose. She did, and seemed to catch on quickly that I couldn't speak, recovering quickly from whatever discomfort by saying something bland about the size of the crowd, still rocking a little to the music, smiling. I decided I liked her.

Of course, I had been anticipating moments like these. I knew my helplessness would encourage an extra layer of social awkwardness, beyond what might normally be expected when navigating a new but intimate setting with hundreds of strangers. Like always, I wished for the ability to manage how I was seen, yet there I was, so skinny, in a wheelchair, barely able to straighten my own shirt or tuck my hair behind my ear, unable to shake a hand or share my name or return a hug. If I drank water, I couldn't hide the drip from my chin after sipping it, and when I ate, I couldn't hide the food falling off my bobbing utensils while my gaping mouth quivered in determination.

Certainly, I could no longer rely on able-bodied privilege to help me blend in. My awkward movements and weakness would encourage some level of spectacle or pity or sympathy from whoever wasn't tracking their own gaze. As a proud person, this was a certain kind of hell. I now knew when people are not busy ignoring those with disabilities altogether due to their own revulsion and fear, many often stare outright, oblivious that there's actually a conscious being inside that assumedly regrettable physical presentation. This is even more true for someone relatively young with a funky haircut and an allegiance to colorful outfits. Like it or not, I would be noticed for being "different."

———

After the first rah-rah lecture by Dr. Joe, meant to encourage us to be open for a week full of life transformation, everyone was assigned to meet in their smaller teams. We filed out of the ballroom, went wandering among hundreds in search of our meeting room, and then filed in and headed to the back so John could stand next to me. Our team leader welcomed the fifty of us, offered some words of excited welcome, and asked us to each briefly introduce ourselves and our intentions for the retreat so we could start making personal connections.

One by one, each person stood and offered a little about themselves, where they're from, if they were new to this work or not, and what illness or issue they wanted to heal. Trying to simultaneously pay attention to the speaker and figure out what to say, I feverishly thumbed an introduction on my phone. I then handed it to John.

By the time it was our turn, I was trembling in anticipation. John announced, "Hello, my name is John, and first, I'm going to read this introduction my wife Teri wrote for you." After a short pause, he began.

"Hi everyone, my name is Teri and I don't currently have a voice with which to speak to you. I'm here to see about saving my life from early-onset neurodegenerative illness. I believe it's possible to heal and get my health back despite what Western medicine might say. Even though I can't really speak, my mind and hearing are not affected, so any of you are welcome to speak to me throughout this week and I will appreciate it and understand."

As he read, feeling the full weight of being stared at by a not-small crowd of strangers. I wanted to hide—especially when the room broke into applause. *Why do I do this?* I wondered. *Why must I keep putting myself out there for everyone to see?*

John then continued, tears quickly forming in his eyes. "Well… I don't know what else to say," he murmured to the expectant stillness in the room. "I… I just love Teri so much… and want to do whatever we can for her."

Overwhelmed by the intimacy of the moment, I then let slip one piercing, uncontainable sob. This show triggered nearly everyone else to start crying as well, evidenced by copious sniffles and gleaming eyes throughout the room. Because my facial muscles had already deteriorated, the act of trying to hold in my tears resulted in a strange grimace. *Here I am, this is me everyone, nice to meet you… and sigh.*

Immediately after the meeting, a small crowd of people approached us to introduce themselves. I wanted badly to get to engage with them with my old voice, so I could bridge the chasm between our realities with words. *See, I'm relatable despite being a crip! And I'm a good-mannered conversationalist who knows how to take interest in you and balance the flow of dialogue!* But I couldn't do this. All I could do was receive their pats and compliments and reassurances by smiling, nodding, offering a squeaky affirmative, *yeah!*, and hope that they could sense my essence beyond words.

———

The week had its distractions. Despite trying to follow instructions to focus only on the vision of total healing, my mind wandered, as minds do. Now, I did the focusing thing for periods—including a four-hour excited one after arising from a powerful meditation with a noticeably stronger voice—but other thoughts always crept in to tug at the corners of my attention: worries about how much work I was for John, wondering if he was getting enough of his own needs for rest met… Questions about whether we should notify anyone that the absence of gender-neutral bathrooms made our lives, and undoubtedly others' lives, really difficult… Concerns about whether I had gone too far in throwing off my food rules for the week (but *oh*, the cappuccinos and pineapple smoothies and farmed shrimp were *so* good, and pleasure is healing, right?)… And, true to form, fears about whether I was really getting "it"—the magical healing formula—at the rate I needed. Of course, I knew that healing wasn't always predictable or fast in nature, but as the most visibly compromised person at the gigantic retreat, I couldn't help but assume I needed to be an A++ student with the biggest, most loudly colorful cosmic orgasms. Via meditation, of course.

The meditations we were doing for hours each day consisted of various breathwork and visualizations. They were largely intended to liberate stuck emotional energy in the body, and for some, this process was intense. Not long into any given session, people around the ballroom would begin to have some version of a cosmic orgasms, or would "pop," as Dr. Joe referred to it. One or five or thirty people would start shaking, sighing, moaning, jerking, or even yelling, unprepared for the amount of energy that was suddenly coursing through their bodies. John was sometimes one of them. As always, my experiences were subtle and quiet; I'd feel some gentle stirring in my heart or throat, often with a certain pleasant calm. The times when nothing much happened, I'd notice the familiar suspicion that I might be the one exception to the rules of healing. I tried to bat this fear away.

But it wasn't until Dr. Joe seemed to get more loose-lipped with us during an afternoon lecture that a stronger doubt took hold in my mind—this time, a doubt that wasn't directed at my ability to follow his instructions, but at the premise behind the instructions themselves. In an effort to encourage us, he exclaimed something that hit me as: "If you're not healing through the meditations—if you aren't reversing your condition—you need to try harder! Do it better! *Be* better! You need to be 'all in.' Don't hold back!"

Wait… WHAT? I gasped internally, glancing at John to see if he'd heard the same thing I had, hoping to share a gnarly expression. Instead he sat in rapt attention. *Did that guy seriously just say that?* I wished I had been drinking something so I could have spit it out for dramatic effect.

Even though I had often saddled myself with outsized responsibility for the outcome of my own healing efforts, to hear someone
else do it with such unequivocal terms triggered an immediate,
visceral balking. Of course I had already dabbled in the wishful
idea of my own omnipotence, which looked like this: *If I could only
follow the right protocols closely enough, eat the right diet, find the right
doctor who orders the right tests or the healer with the right therapy, do
enough research on the mechanisms of health and disease, pray or think
or meditate or visualize strong and often enough, then I'd figure out
this riddle of disease and finally get back what I most desired: my fully
functioning body, and the life I* should *be living.* And, of course, the
dark dualistic underbelly to this prosperity-gospel line of thinking
was, *If I fail to reverse my health, it's solely my own fault. I have failed.
I am the failure.* Ouch.

When taken in context of rumors that some people had even
regrown severed limbs through visualization—"Anything is healable!"—it sounded an awful lot like blame for those who don't heal
their condition. It sounded like an oversimplifying of the complex
forces that could affect outcomes in illness. It sounded like an
encouragement for a God complex, playing to the timeless human
wishes for ultimate control. It sounded like an ableist assumption
that any "abnormal" condition should be healed, because at the root
of things, disability is unacceptable, an aberration.

Suddenly my complaints about New Age blame and shame
flooded back in full force. Throwing off all efforts to follow the
lecture, I wondered what kind of mental gymnastics it takes to claim
to a huge roomful of hungry people that meditation alone should
be enough to create their preferred realities. What if some of these
people have unaddressed trauma? What if they need addiction

treatment, or have lead in their water supply, or are deficient in magnesium because the soils have been stripped by industrial agriculture? We don't fault the leaves who fall first from the trees, saying "they should have tried harder, been more 'all in,'" because we know the leaves of trees are aspects of a much larger system—affected by soil, by genetics, by injury, by weather patterns and beetles and ecosystems, so don't us humans deserve similar considerations? As social animals, our health and well-being can never be separated from the webs in which we're held. Forget bootstraps; we need good relationships and safety nets, good healthcare and corporate accountability. Even among the able-bodied and most privileged, independence is a radical myth; we all rely on others to pick and ship the papaya for our detox smoothies, among a thousand other daily transactions.

I thought of how some manifestation gurus and alternative health experts fall ill or die young despite their teachings on our abilities to create our own destinies through enough affirmations or belief or gratitude. Are we to believe an inability to transform matter is ultimately a failure of imagination or effort? What if some people's deepest life tasks have more to do with developing the virtues of perseverance, adaptation, or making peace with limitation, rather than manifesting what capitalist society claims as an acceptable (read: productive) body or life?

But I also suspected metaphysical gurus don't become wealthy celebrities packing huge ballrooms by offering nuanced arguments about the reach of our personal power; that they usually do it by reducing reality into slick promises of our own total self-determination. Whether they back their arguments up by purportedly channeling ascended masters, or using simple four-question processes which can't in themselves be questioned if they don't "Work," or becoming psychic YouTube starlets who use sex appeal to cement a cult following, the basic message is the same: "The problems are not in the world or your body so much as in your own head. Just change your perceptions or vibration enough, and everything heals. Systemic realities don't have power unless you allow them to."

I knew some of these metaphysical teachers—usually bathed in unacknowledged white, well-off privilege—would even go so far as to say individuals or racial/ethnic groups who've experienced violence or dislocation "manifested" it because of their own masochism or sense of unworthiness. And though it all sounded like the ultimate cultural gaslighting to me, I knew critical thinking in response to any narcissistic or cultic narrative can be conveniently written off as small-minded resistance, perhaps signifying the need to do more "work" on a doubting or "oversensitive" ego. To which I fantasized offering a very enlightened barf.

At the time, I didn't know that when I'd gently raise these thoughts in online Dr. Joe discussion groups after the retreat, my posts would swiftly get deleted. Nor did I know that within another six months Dr. Joe would announce he was beginning to sell nutritional supplements purportedly designed to support the body during meditation. Blatant money-making opportunity aside, in my mind this course change acknowledged that sometimes, we need something beyond our own good intentions and visions; we need actual physical intervention. And if it's the case that taking synthetic supplements can make it more likely for someone to relax during a low-stakes meditation, wouldn't it also be true that physical interventions can sometimes be a necessary component for someone dealing with a complicated disease?

But even prior to this future change of tune on his part, I could have seen this moment of dissonance coming during the retreat. Despite *wanting* to believe, I was already awash in conflict toward the manifestation narrative. The heightened stress of my prognosis had kicked me even further into self-protective mode, fighting off the implicit message that if one is "good" enough they get rewarded with healing. One, I wanted to fight back against the very premise that piling outsized responsibility on top of a debilitating illness was ever helpful—even if it's cloaked in #loveandlight, and #itsallgood. And two, it hadn't worked for me anyway.

But though Dr. Joe's words sat heavily in the moment, I willed my grievance to behave. Already having sunk so much into the trip, I wasn't about to toss the opportunity to see what new breakthroughs in perspective could still happen because I felt his framework was guilty of overreaching human spheres of control. For all I know he simply drank too much wine over lunch and got sloppier than intended in delivery, or I simply projected onto him what he didn't actually say, or mean. This meant that in the coming days John and I could just try to enjoy ourselves, no matter the ultimate outcome. It was a beautiful setting, after all; it was warm and sunny, the food was good, we were making new friends to share meals with. We even spotted chattering young monkeys eating bananas one night on the hotel balcony. So every time my doubts about the whole venture crept in, I batted them away. *Just. Stay. Present.*

———

Midway through the week, our team had a challenge course activity on hotel property. Everyone would get an opportunity to do a high trust fall, or walk a tightrope, or rappel down a wall, and John, bless him, did all three. From my seat on the sidelines I witnessed his exhilaration, so happy he had some moments all to himself which had nothing to do with me or my illness. I felt so proud of him. Despite him having to watch his hoped-for future with me steadily slip away, despite the exhaustion of having to show up for me physically, mentally, and emotionally moment after moment, he somehow managed to take this opportunity to engage in voluntary challenges of a different nature, simply because he was committed to stretching himself even more. So I cried with a swollen heart.

To the course staff's credit, I got my chance to be "challenged" too, which would take some creativity on their part. They set up a special adaptive trust fall, where I'd be tipped backward in my chair, and then caught inches before my back and head hit the ground. One would think I was doing something significant by the size of the crowd that circled around to cheer me on.

After a slow tilt backward with catchers on both sides, I came up to a roar of clapping, followed by a stream of people approaching to tell me how brave I was. This was sweet, but I noted it had been more courageous to have the four guys pick up my rickety wheelchair and carry me down the ten narrow, rain-slicked stairs to the course. Now *that* took trust, on all our parts. And no one had clapped.

But this idealized, perhaps outsized attention was by now becoming a theme. I'd been witnessing an interesting vulnerability/attraction phenomenon take place all week, as if my earnest efforts, weakness, and struggle were a colorful bird's mating dance on full display. Just by showing up, I had attracted new friends of all ages and races and genders approaching me with kind words of admiration or offers to help. The attention was varied, and often seemed to happen in or after especially vulnerable moments: there was the unfamiliar young man who wanted to help steady me in the crowded lobby when John was away using the bathroom, who I ignored in his gentle efforts to brace my chair while I shakily stood to stretch my stiff legs. *Dude, you're nice, but just let me struggle alone!* Or there was the older man who saw me in tears during our team's challenge course and decided what I most needed after a short introduction was a long, slow kiss on the lips. (For the record, this wasn't what I most needed.) Some strangers would come up to gaze deeply into my eyes and tell me I'm beautiful, suddenly reaching out to stroke my face or cup my chin. *Whoa, pardner! Boundaries still apply!* Mostly, I tried to just receive whatever good intentions others might be feeling for me, as intrusive as their actions might be and as much as I lacked the ability to signal consent to sudden intimacy.

Perhaps these folks would idealize anyone willing to show up and be seen so physically "un-healed" in a setting intended for radical healing; I don't know. Even in other public settings, well-meaning people can bend over backward to show how impressed they are by us disabled folks being willing to show up; "You're so brave! I'd surely just hide." We provide inspiration porn; that's how we roll.

But it felt more than that. When my team leader came up to me after a strong meditation at the end of the week and said, "I love you, Teri," and gave me a big embrace, it felt good, and true. Never mind that I had just met him. I was open because it seemed to be offered with one notion at the core: love itself is healing. Recognition is healing. Care is healing. And it's all so very human.

In a way, all these interactions were dancing with the reality that as strangers—and given circumstances where we're not competing for power or safety—we can sometimes feel great attraction to one another due to our shared humanity and basic care for other beings. Sometimes just existing in our vulnerability, being courageously seen in our open display of our human shakiness, becomes a gift to others. Perhaps it gives them permission to love that which is still tender and unformed in themselves. Hopefully, this tenderness translates into a more open heart toward everything boldly, imperfectly, unapologetically itself, in its finite and irreplaceable essence. And *also* hopefully, this love translates into advocacy for things like damn good access ramps.

As for the challenge course, the questions it was designed to bring up—*What if I fall? Will the others catch me? Can I put my well-being in their hands? Is the landing beneath me steady? Can I really show up for this challenge?*—were ones I grappled with literally and figuratively every day before lunch, without the benefit of fancy helmets and harnesses and pep talks. But before I let myself get too puffed up by my superior-courage-complex, I remembered: we're all vulnerable to misfortune all of the time, whether we are willing to admit it or not. We never truly know which safety ropes will hold and which will snap. We will inevitably lose our footing sometimes. And yet if we hear the call, we learn to show up anyway, to put ourselves on the plank for everyone to witness. Our days themselves are the course into which we must leap, with no guaranteed cushion to break our freefall. Except, perhaps, the advocacy and attention of those nearby and the web they weave to support us.

My most significant moment of surrender that week would arise, all irony aside, during a walking meditation. Dr. Joe had all 900 of us convene on the beach at 4:15 A.M. to meditate with the sunrise. We were instructed to wear our headphones while listening to the prerecorded instructions on embodying our future selves. After some sleepy arguing about the best place to put me, John and I agreed to a paved area at the top of the main stairway leading down to the beach. He placed my headphones on, kissed me, removed his shoes, kissed me again, and strutted down the stairs to his own sandy adventure.

The instructions offered to all of us non-walking participants were simple: just imagine walking by feeling the accompanying emotions and sensations it would include, which would thereby activate similar areas of the brain. And sure enough, I soon felt my arms swinging and heart pumping and cold sand squishing between my toes. Embodying the simple pleasure of walking freely along a beach again caused tears of exhilaration and gratitude to flow freely.

But as the sun began to creep up the ocean horizon, my imaginings transformed from walking in the future, to a real-time experience of unconditional safety. It's as if the fundamental goodness of the waves and sand and trees, all these hungry, quirky people, my own windswept skin and gathering tears and precious legs—strong or not—was made undeniable. More, this basic brilliance of life itself yearned for *my* conscious recognition of its creative beauty.

As the meditation hour ended, and the participants started streaming up the stairs to retrieve their shoes, hundreds of them passed within feet of me. Feeling all those eyes on me prompted me to want to pull it together and hide with shame from whatever judgments they might make. But instead, something hesitant and shy inside broke open. *Fuck it*, I thought. *Let them witness my surrendered love embrace with life.* So there I sat, limp paws to heart, heaving with freely streaming tears, allowing my big goofy grin to be warmed by the rising sun, being seen by who knows who. And something prone to hiding deep inside, which hadn't yet seen light in this lifetime, began to thaw in the radiant gaze of the sun.

Days later, after we'd finally had a stumbly dip in one of the pools, after sharing a virgin pina colada on the beach, after hugging our new friends goodbye, it was time to return home. And somewhere in that process, I began to ponder a question. Could it be possible to find peace with my situation, not because I personally engineered or deserve it, but because there might be something sacred unfolding anyway? Perhaps there was something greater happening; something trustworthy. Even something intimate worth delighting in and relaxing with, right here and now, whether or not my legs would ever carry me for another walk.

17.
Making Offerings

SPRING 2019

Upon returning home from Mexico, and despite my reservations with his approach, I continued with Dr. Joe's meditations. Most days I sat up to three or four hours, squeezing as much wishful enthusiasm for life as my deeply conflicted heart could muster. Nonetheless, as the weeks wore on I felt myself getting weaker, which meant some inner whispers were getting louder which I really, *really* wished to ignore.

So it takes me ten minutes to shuffle between the bedroom and the living room with my walker? *Big deal, at least I can still walk.* So my manual wheelchair is uncomfortable and rickety and requires someone to push me around? *It's low-key and fits the need in a pinch.* But as my knees began buckling every time I tried to stand, and the slightest surprise could cause a deep wobble in my balance and threaten a nosedive, I begrudgingly admitted to myself that I needed more help. Meaning, I would soon need an electric wheelchair, aka powerchair.

Like with most tools meant to support a disabled body, I resisted caving to it for as long as possible. But of all the potential aids to help me—braces, walkers, gripping tools, speech devices, shower chairs, manual wheelchairs—the powerchair seemed by far the most vile. Built to support the weakened neck as seen in neuromuscular conditions, they are bulky, expensive, and—to that part of me still under sway of ableist prejudice—decidedly ugly. On the websites advertising them I found photos of young, attractive, ostensibly disabled people sitting in various models while enjoying exciting disabled-people activities, such as *sitting*, flashing excited smiles for no apparent reason. The text highlighted the freedom they provide their users.

My various healthcare providers would talk them up too, and encouraged me to move forward in ordering one so I could start enjoying it. I suspected "enjoy" was just polite code for the mobility I would gain courtesy of the hand-operated joystick, allowing me to safely navigate wheelchair accessible spaces. But the thought of one signaled to me the opposite of delighted freedom—more like defining submission. Not to mention this kind of tool tends to frighten strangers, who suddenly turn awkward when beholding someone operating heavy machinery to move their body around. Through submitting to one, I would turn into the "trapped" man I first saw in the neurology waiting room of the university hospital. The man who I didn't want to make eye contact with. The man who I had been terrified to someday become.

By this stage I knew that I needed to advance toward each milestone of my ever-changing physical reality slowly, lest I invite a freshly debilitating round of grief and crankiness. So I set up for the ALS Association to deliver a temporary loaner with the intent for it to just sit in our living room for days so I could get used to looking at it. On the morning that the technician delivered the 250-pound beast, I tried to just soften my gaze around it, not asking many questions, trying to keep an eye toward distractions like lunch approaching and emails to send. My caregiver signed the loaner paperwork and waved him away for me, leaving us alone with the new monster. There it would sit for the next few days, lurking menacingly against our living-room wall, waiting for me to work up the nerve to dare to sit in it. I swore I heard it growl once or twice.

But our cat saw nothing monstrous about the new addition to our family. Once the technician left, Anu spent a few minutes sniffing all the unfamiliar crevices and features, as if he was a discriminating buyer inspecting a big potential purchase. Soon satisfied with whatever mystery his little nose sorted out, he then hopped onto the seat, circled around once or twice to arrange his body, plopped down with an air of relaxed contentment, and sighed. He slowly batted his tail over the armrest, blinking pointedly at me, glancing out the nearest window, yawning, threatening an imminent nap. I'd soon admit he had found his new preferred perch in our home, and noted he stayed there as much as possible during the coming days, occasionally rolling onto his back to expose his velvety belly, throw a wayward paw into the air, and purr. King Anupalaya, administering from a fancy throne worth $15,000—how fitting. My little protector.

Eventually, I caught on to his teaching—or at least what my humor entertained as his teaching. His attitude suggested my revulsion to the chair might not be required. Of course, all the strong emotions I brought to it were understandable because I'm invested in the details of my life. He's an admittedly spoiled and strong-limbed cat just taking a nap, which is a temporary reprieve between begging loudly for more kitty-crack treats and galloping throughout the house, triumphant after a good poo. And yet, if I chose to entertain the possibility of a message, like how when you relax your mind enough you can make any tarot reading feel true, he seemed to suggest I had more choice in how I received the new tool than I thought.

I could practice viewing it as a comfy, practical place to sit; a place which made it easy to look out the window, relax, philosophize, like Anu—or, unlike Anu, even go outside and get around. I could learn to reject the narrative that says using a wheelchair somehow makes one less-than or pitiable compared to non-wheelchair users. Rather than being "trapped by" or "confined to," I could view it as my own throne that helps me live a full, active life, for as long as possible. Yet another reminder that I could deepen my own suffering by steadily focusing on the wrongness of a situation, instead of an earthy practicality: life was providing me a new viewpoint, from a thickly padded seat no less. Meaning-making was flexible, and resistance was optional.

———

Meanwhile, it was becoming increasingly clear that we needed to leave the apartment. It was cramped, visitors had no place to sleep, and the rent and random fees were increasing with every opportunity. But our requirements for a place to live were not simple. We needed an affordable and wheelchair-accessible home with no history of water damage, which meant it would need to be fairly new. And we knew that "new" plus "affordable" was not a likely equation for the Boulder housing market.

Unlikely, that is, until I remembered that we had the option of finding a mobile home. The light bulb in my head suddenly clicked on one day, and the idea made instant sense. We had rented one before getting married, and had enjoyed the simplicity and rustic, camper-like feel, even finding the neighborhood a friendly oasis from Boulder's uncommonly monochrome and increasingly posh, speedy, entitled vibe.

Within a week of beginning the search, I came across a listing for a light-filled manufactured home with an open floor plan on the edge of town. The owner got back to my questions right away, assuring me there had never been water damage to the home since he had installed it brand new a year prior. What's more, he recognized my name, confessed to being an old coworker of John's, and was happy to show it to us before the open house. It turned out to be exactly what we had hoped. Within a month of light negotiations, financial juggling, and packing up our tiny apartment, it was time to move in.

Only one problem: there was no ramp to get me in. Fortunately, in Cancun we had learned anything was possible with enough strong backs around, so I emailed a handful of our friends to meet us at the front porch on move day to carry me up the five entrance steps in my manual chair. My mother was visiting to help with the move, and she made a big show of the four guys carrying me across the threshold of our new home. She insisted on taking picture after picture on her smartphone, even as my eye rolling "Mommm!"

whines didn't deter her. She said loudly, "What? You told me to take pictures of the cute guys!" In my mind, that conversation had gone like this:

Mom: "I'll take pictures of the move."

Me, shrugging: "Ummm… okay."

Her generous rewrite of history resulted in my first face blush in years. How mothers can make us act like embarrassed fifteen-year-olds when we're already well into adulthood remains one of humanity's timeless mysteries.

Still, the most immediate hurdle had been conquered. Thanks to the service of our hunky friends, I was now in the house. And it was a definite upgrade. I now had my choice of sunny rooms to be in, which makes a big difference for an easily annoyed introvert who relies on caregivers yet likes existing behind closed doors. We would now have a guest bedroom, which would be useful when family visited. And, like everyone loved to remind me, it should now be easier to write my book in uninterrupted privacy. *Right…* that *thing*.

———

Sometime late into 2018, roughly six months prior to the move, some close friends had begun urging me to write a book chronicling my journey through the illness. They had read some of my writing and thought it would be worth sharing with a larger audience. I thanked them for the votes of confidence and reassured them that I would maybe consider doing it. Someday.

This was not a wholly new idea. Like most adults will admit to, I had previously fantasized about someday writing a book, and now I finally had an improbable story to tell. Maybe this would be my Persephone offering after flirting with death, I thought. But in imagining the proper circumstances under which to make such an effort, I reckoned I should be on the physical upswing, having made a triumphant return to the land of the living, and ready to start round two of my blessed story. After all, everyone loves tales of stunning and improbable comebacks. All I had to do, I reasoned, was wait until that magical day of redemption would come for me.

But my friends are no fools, and therefore never seemed too satisfied with my passive procrastination. Their reminders started sounding increasingly naggy and urgent. I argued back, *I will, when and if I'm better! Because who would want to hop on the literary train of an unremarkable white middle-class thirty-something who fought like hell against a terrible disease, yet just died anyway? I mean, besides my own mother? How exactly is that inspiring?* It seemed obvious that in compulsively optimistic, bootstrapping, youth-oriented American culture, a story chronicling a drawn-out death via paralysis doesn't exactly make the hordes line up, whimpering in anticipatory rapture.

But after getting three increasingly stern messages within the space of one week to start writing anyway, *goshdarnit,* I decided that someone or something was trying like heck to deliver a message through my thick skull. So the first few chapters were tapped out on my phone in January of 2019, until even my thumbs became too floppy from muscle loss to write anything coherent. I then awkwardly held a padded stylus to our tablet—not unlike the way a toddler might stranglefist a crayon—until that, too, became just indecipherable slaps at the screen within another month. After my speech therapist fully trained me on my new fancy Tobii Dynavox eye-gaze computer mounted near my chair, I switched to typing via an onscreen keyboard which could read my pupils and blinks. I'd slowly click... click... click... one letter at a time for three, five, ten hours a day, my eyes burning from mechanized effort well into the evening, punctuated only by periodic breaks for all the funny cat videos my Facebook feed would offer.

And thus began the long journey of highs and lows common for anyone attempting a large creative endeavor. Or, at least, any endeavor which holds potential to expose one's failings and blind spots to everyone they've ever known. John quickly adjusted to the cycle of me professing my enthusiasm for the ambitious project, only to be interrupted every few days by dramatic spirals of self-doubt: "What a farce! I'm not a real writer. I'll be remembered as that naive woman-child who recorded a bunch of cliché reflections right before dying. Nearly everyone I know is a frigging therapist! I'll be awarded diagnoses posthumously! *The shame!* I can't." If we had a fainting couch, I would have requested he drape me on it so I could continue. "What if it doesn't help anyone? Will it lead people astray somehow? Do I even believe this flowery shit I'm writing?" And, the most important question of all: "What if all the swearing offends my Midwestern in-laws?"

In reply to my fears which cascaded every week or two, John would offer an exasperated, "Oh babe. This again? You just need to write it! Write! Who cares?" Sometimes he'd just sigh heavily, trusting I knew exactly what he meant. Occasionally I remembered my favorite saying on narcissism, and chuckle about being the biggest piece of shit the whole world revolves around.

Okay, okay. Clearly I couldn't always trust my inner bully, meaning I probably needed to put on my big-girl pants and do this *thing* that I felt compelled to do, disregarding whatever criticisms and relational weirdness might eventually come my way for it. Besides, in less terrified moments I could remember the book wasn't so much about *me* anyway; it's about universal themes of loss, determination, and revisioning, and simply uses my story so that my hard-won lessons might actually be put to use for other's benefit. That's how it works.

A couple years before the illness took hold, I had begun uttering an intention—a prayer, really—in quiet and inspired moments. Spoken aloud on high desert walks near the Crestone retreat center I frequented, or in the short space between clients at my office, or at the end of my meditation sessions in hopes of setting the focus for the day, it was simple enough: "Let me be of service." Occasionally I'd shiver from the strength of the desire to help others, to encourage them to relate well to their emotions and maybe even relax a little into trusting life's challenges. In some of my more doe-eyed moments, perhaps seduced by Bodhisattva aspirations, I even felt willing to sacrifice my life in whatever way the fates might deem best to go about fulfilling that intention. Looking back on my dreams of Persephone, I think only, *Doh! Nice idea; poorly designed. Forgot the "except for Hades" clause.*

But, of course, it's hard to predict how our own experience of suffering might eventually transmute into a service to others. Or how to quantify when it's worth the price.

In the midst of writing, for example, I had moments of despair and cynicism strong enough that I'd question the whole outrageous premise of gifts coming from pain. While Gabriella made it sound so tidy and simple and automatic, I knew that it's somewhere between difficult and impossible to *actually* mine gifts from loss—especially the types of losses which cause a shattering, complicated grief. And pressure doesn't always yield diamonds; the alternate outcomes of despair and bitterness and even mental illness are also possible, just as enough poverty, injustice, and trauma can exhaust and darken any people's or person's spirits.

Since Reggie had offered me beautiful teachings alongside bypassing narratives cloaked in universal compassion, I was certain that I didn't want to perpetuate the dissociation I had been schooled in by studying with him. In a book about illness that I knew in all likelihood will be terminal, I feared the "diamond" metaphor could glamorize suffering or martyrdom. While it's tempting to want to turn everything into a feel-good story, to wrap it all up in a tidy little package topped with a bow—especially because narratives of pretty resolution sell books like nobody's business—doing so would be a disservice to everyone out there who understandably struggles with the seeming meaninglessness of their suffering, whether they're sick or not. So during a period where I invited title ideas from friends, one suggested the non-promising, *I Wrote This With My Fucking Eyeballs; You Should Read it With Yours*, which I considered a safe premise for my story.

The suspicion of pain being needless and irredeemable was most pronounced for me when considering those who I would be leaving behind if indeed I was headed for an early death, a likelihood which steadily grew more real month by month. I wondered why my aging parents would lose their only daughter at the exact time they would need me to start supporting them. Why my brother would be dealt this grief on top of everything else challenging in his life. Why John would be widowed when he's so young, from an even younger wife, no less. *Where's the effing "gift" in that?* And since their pain would be caused by me, I felt guilty. Meaning-making seemed futile.

When I shared these feelings with my close friend Doris on an afternoon she visited, she nodded patiently, validating my swooning at the injustice. Finally, she asked, "What would you say to someone else who felt that guilt?"

I paused, imagining the luxury of an outside perspective. I then typed into my speech device, "I'd ask them how they knew their illness and death was not also a service instead of just a tragic loss for their loved ones."

Apparently, that was a good answer, because Doris, bless her, jumped out of her seat and squealed "Yessssss!" with a fist pump or two. With my mouth gaping in surprise that she was so delighted, we both promptly burst into laughter.

In retrospect I could acknowledge that would very rarely be a good answer in real life, and could border on cruel, bypassy dismissal of someone in pain. It's not the *death* that's the gift, but the precious life that came before it. But we were getting philosophical, geeking out on soul-level perspective.

The thing that excited Doris so much was the idea that trusting life as it unfolds ultimately requires us to trust each other's resilience. With the right support and inspiration, those of us who experience great heartbreak can end up capable of swimming in deeper waters without having to fear imminent drowning. Assuming we *want* to try to identify silver linings—because doing so speaks to a fairly persistent human urge for meaning-making, revisioning, and fortitude—we may identify internal and often subtle gifts: more humility, more perspective, more reverence for the irreplaceable. And if we're lucky (or perhaps wise), more empathy for others and forgiveness for ourselves, and a newfound reckoning for how we want to live in this precious impermanence.

Throughout this illness, I witnessed transformations in those closest to me. Though I was the one with the symptoms, everyone was presented an opportunity to grow. And if our cosmology allows for the belief that we all signed up for this wild, complicated, beautiful, wrenching human journey, then it's not our job to protect others from the heartbreak which accompanies the inevitable loss of what we hold most dear, including each other. Though these losses are real and piercing, there are always other wise, competent forces available to hold others if and when we cannot, whether other family, therapists, mentors, support groups, the big trees, the nearest ocean, or whatever or whomever their higher powers may be. We never could guarantee anything for anyone else anyway—this is just part of the planet Earth package. And, we never know how wide their hearts might grow in the process of enduring unavoidable pain and challenge, and who they might ultimately become as a result.

———

As I wrote, I sifted through all I had learned so far. Once I got comfortable using my powerchair and had the space of our new home to navigate, I'd roll from room to room throughout each day, looking for the best spot to write in two-hour jags. Preferably it was quiet, held the right breeze-to-warmth ratio, yet lacked direct light and glare which prevented my computer from reading my squinting eyes. Sometimes Anu would hop onto my lap and purr encouragement; sometimes I'd request the door be shut behind me. And in the hundreds of hours that I drafted and redrafted my story, I sweated and cursed and cried, squeezed by my own grief and conflict and gratitude. The effort of willing something beautiful and true to arise from all of it was occasionally punishing. Eventually, I realized the depth and darkness and pressure of diamond making felt true, so I mined it all as best I could, imperfectly, in an attempt to offer companionship to those facing their own dark night.

It seems this is what service is about: offering whatever we can of ourselves, and then getting out of the way for whatever may or may not come of it. Because when our heart and tears and honesty are in something, others feel it, and I imagine the enthusiasm for what we offer transmits some cosmic love cologne as a gift both for them and for us; in which case we can't *not* love giving. The important part, it seems, is doing what we're called to do in our quieter moments—the thing that gives us a deep, earthy yes, which may be accompanied by relief at knowing our path, and terror at stepping wholeheartedly onto it. Perhaps our awkward but sincere efforts along the way are all that's called for; perhaps they give others permission to do the same.

18.
Sacred Anger

SUMMER 2019

n early June, my mother came to relieve John from my care so
he could attend a clinical training course in Scottsdale. When
he had first announced his desire to attend this training, a year
prior, I felt grumbly, yet I reasoned it was fair that he would need
an occasional break from the rigors of caring for me. I wanted to
be that kind of easy-going, low-maintenance wife, even if only in
theory and for a weekend.

But sure enough, once he kissed me goodbye and walked
through our front door, his absence soon became glaringly loud.
Overnight I was minimally capable of adjusting the covers with
my own heavy limbs, so I alternated between being flaming hot
in a twisted burrito of sheets, or overexposed and shivering. With
my mom down the hall in the guest room, I couldn't cry out loudly
enough for help. The next morning, once I had been plopped onto

the toilet by her, I learned that she was insufficiently trained on the updated restroom protocol, which had been carefully designed to maximize whatever privacy and dignity I could still be awarded. What's more, she forgot how to properly use the spelling board so I could instruct her on the spot through eye blinks when she pointed to certain letters—our backup communication tool for emergencies—and she also failed to figure out she could *read the simple instructions* on the back of it. With no voice to explain what to do, my frustration hit fever pitch. *Think, Mom!* I shrieked internally. *Be the adult! Help me!* In my powerlessness I began shaking with a primal rage, not unlike a furious toddler who just so happens to have a wickedly precocious internal dialogue.

Well, "furious" could have been the surface-level diagnosis. Kind of like how "ALS" is really just a progressing outcome of symptoms from an aggregation of unique causes, I knew by now that "anger" usually includes a combination of vulnerable emotions and unmet needs. And in this case, I had a stew: the fear of physical mishaps; the worry that my mother wouldn't be able to address those mishaps when they took place; the hurt that she still couldn't take charge in the one way I most wanted; the dismay that she had to deal with caring for my 38-year-old self at all; the hurt that John would leave me when I needed him; the unease that accompanied having my privacy exposed; the impatience with feeling so not in control... and on and on. It didn't matter that my mom had great intentions, that the immediate tasks might be difficult for anyone, that if I thought about it, I knew she would eventually figure it out and the moon would again rise. What mattered in the moment was that I was overwhelmed with helplessness, and therefore felt insulted as *a being.* The resulting rush of "fight" energy desperately demanded the restoration of the control and dignity and safety which appeared lost. I reminded myself, of course I was furious; just because the limbic brain doesn't speak rationally, doesn't mean it defies all logic.

—

Like so many of us, my relationship with anger had often been fraught with confusion and judgment. Anger—and its myriad hues including irritation, annoyance, punishing withdrawal, all the way to aggression, hostility, cold contempt, and hot fury—had always felt dangerous and even shameful, whether expressed through me or someone else. And if we're "good" people, trying to live a conscious, generous life, we're going to be easy-going, infinitely trusting, and quick to forgive, right? *Ha. A fucking serenity sandwich.*

So when a retreat leader in Peru told me that in her experience, students of Buddhism typically held a lot of buried anger, I suddenly saw the light: *Of course we do.* And what better way to avoid it by spending our time in meditation trying to soften the hard edges of our feelings, dropping our thoughts, and going on retreats that limit our interactions with other pesky people and their endlessly annoying needs and behaviors? What a peaceful setting to try to shake off our ego, and what is anger if not red-hot ego? It also doesn't help that many of us within Buddhist traditions end up taking the Bodhisattva vow, wherein we may confuse emotional repression and denial of one's own needs for enlightened generosity. *Check.*

Other traditions have their own styles of denying and repressing feelings, and after living and working in Boulder for a decade, I'd seen it all. This conflict around anger seemed especially true for *anyone* who fancies themselves "spiritual"; perhaps doubly so for women, with all the sticky messages about how to hold in the reins of assertion lest we be thought hysterical bitches. Many sensitive souls seem to blame themselves for having any feelings other than joy and gratitude, as if they should just swallow anything difficult and always trust life is an all-giving nanny with only their best interests in mind; some think their hurts are solely consequences of their limited perceptions, and if they could only drop their needs enough, be easy-going enough, they could avoid getting down into the dirty muck of communication with other flawed beings. They would rather stay so clean, so pristine, so "above," so self-contained… in other words, much less human.

But more than just those who turn to spirituality and faux positivity to hide from real life—an *anti*-spirituality, I'd eventually decide—anyone raised with confusing messages about the legitimacy of certain basic desires and needs is going to be crafty in denying emotions which might be deemed inappropriate or unseemly. And since buried feelings resist domestication, they end up oozing out sideways through caustic judgments of others, confusing communications, passive-aggression, or self-harm in a hundred different flavors, including perfectionism.

Of course, I had long exercised all kinds of ooze. Like frightened children often do, I skipped over my "fight" instincts for "freeze," swallowing the difficult feelings whole so they could play out in the more manageable arena of my own belly/psyche. This "playing dead" helped foster a sense of control in an impossible scenario. This was a temporarily wise survival strategy.

But for better or worse, as I grew older, something began thawing inside. I watched my anger start to emerge in surprising ways, as if a giant belch of bitter fists suddenly burst from my gut. These outward displays of aggression were ceremoniously kicked off at age seventeen, on a day not unlike many others, when my father happened to be mocking me for being a dumb female with dumb female problems. In this case, menstruation—or so he assumed, if his exaggerated eyeroll and high-pitched reference to my having hormones had anything to do with it. Inspired by Rush Limbaugh, some variation of "dumb woman" had long been his favorite insult toward those of us shameless enough to be gendered female and audacious enough to open our mouths despite it. But instead of offering my standard dirty look and retreating to my bedroom on this particular Friday afternoon, he and my silently observing mother were stunned when they were met with my spontaneous, guttural, piercing scream that somehow escaped both my throat and my better judgment. It lasted a good ten seconds. And... *Wow.* Even the framed family photos on the walls seemed frozen in shocked attention, the silence only broken by my father's two-handed lunge for my neck. By some mercy, Dad loosened his grip after a long few seconds of wrangling, and I managed to escape through the front door for a solo weekend getaway.

Despite my father's best attempt to teach my voice box a lesson in respect, it's safe to say I emerged from adolescence with a temper, and even a tendency to antagonize when in the right mood. The strange men I didn't appreciate getting close to me on the dance floors of my early twenties were occasionally given a too-hard shove backward; the few policemen I interacted with in my adulthood were boldly and unwisely challenged; and eventually, a caregiver who couldn't contain her passive aggression was finally met with my very direct "Fuck you!", the vocal clarity of which surprised us both, and resulted in her abandoning me in the middle of the afternoon. *Oops*. Apparently, I'd evolved into what some might call an equal-opportunity bitch.

While my urge to set boundaries wasn't wrong in these types of scenarios, my adrenalized reactions were impulsive, sometimes violent, and occasionally escalated the immediate threats to all involved. Nonetheless, I've since looked back on this scream at my father—all momentary consequences be damned—as a healthy developmental milestone. It was a crude start to voicing something which everyone should eventually learn how to say—or in some situations, scream—in their own defense: "Enough! I've had enough! Stop that!" If we had somehow hung framed photos of my future therapists on the walls of my childhood home instead of family, they might have broken into Harry Potter-style applause.

Years later I've come to learn why some therapists tend to view fiery, openly combative patients as more psychologically robust than obedient and depressed ones: the combative ones have at least developed well enough to turn their anger outward instead of collapsing it inward. Once any of my clients graduated from weighty, passive depression or numbness to directly expressing anger, including anger toward me, I celebrated. *Hooray! Movement! Lemme have it! Tell me more!* It was no coincidence that I found myself an adoring student of modern psychoanalysis, and the aggression-loving camp of visionary analyst Hyman Spotnitz. I learned that directly, cleanly expressed anger has an energy signaling a powerful will to live. It's capable of demanding positive change. It can defend who and what we love. It's the healthy part of the self, capable of standing up to the bully, inner or outer, and saying, "No. This is the boundary."

I also grew to know the ability to use clean, clear assertion has huge implications for our mental, physical, and collective well-being. Because where would any society end up if no one ever felt enough righteous anger to protest injustice or advocate for necessary socio-cultural shifts? If people know of but aren't angry about systemic racism, runaway climate change, growing rates of homelessness, polluted seas, and leaders who don't care to acknowledge any of it, are they actually in touch with their own conscience and heart? It seems the whole idea of non-violent resistance rests on our moral and ethical compass asserting: *This is wrong. I object! And I have the necessary will and passion—indeed, the love for what is right and true—to show you just how much, consequences be damned.* Heck, even Jesus and Mother Teresa got angry in their search for justice. Maybe it's just part of the package that comes with human life: taxes, anger, and death. Or maybe, more contemporary human life: taxes, anger, death, spiritual bypassing, and climate change, although not always in that order.

Either way, it took years of therapy to learn how to ride the energy of powerful emotion, discern between feeling and fact, and bite the urges to say or do provocative things even if I'm comfortable with intensity. With the help of mindfulness practices, moment by tiny moment, I learned to witness my stories and sensations with a non-judgmental awareness, which bought some distance from my impulses. *There's a hard band across my chest. My jaw is tight. I want to scream... but I don't have to scream... Oh, I'm actually... so, so sad... and terrified things won't work out.* Sometimes I remember to look for the spots of safety and calm within my own body, or a sliver of sanity, humor, or workability within the interaction. And when I do, I find a more useful response.

It seems this is what growing up is all about: building a little more flexibility into the tense moments in our lives, pausing a little more before we respond, remaining a little more centered in our hearts despite the physical, emotional, and moral discomforts life throws our way. Especially if we're blessed by access to good human support, we can grow our abilities to choose our responses, finding ever more creativity in how we express courage. These little victories are the fuel of our own evolution, and our own evolution inspires others. And life—endless trickster that it is—never tires in handing us new challenges to practice with.

———

After being diagnosed and throughout the illness progression, my anger took turns attaching to nearly anything that moved. Despite the decade of work I'd already done to release rage and various resentments, it was like the remaining bandages of coping suddenly got ripped off, and a geyser of hot energy came gushing forth, picking up steam with each new revelation. It went like this:

I was angry at the bacteria or mycotoxins or metals or suicidal mitochondria or *whatever* was quickly ravishing my precious body, who clearly gave zero regard to my boundaries. I was angry at the arrogant doctors, the ignorant doctors, the doctors who didn't have time for my research or questions or concerns. Angry at the reluctance of conventional medicine to draw obvious connections between the health of our bodies and the health of our environments, and giving little heed to the possibility of chronic infections and toxins underlying deadly disease; for effectively abandoning those of us already slapped with untreatable diagnoses, often refusing to treat comorbidities because we're "just going to die anyway."

I was angry that my insurer would slap me with a $26K+ bill for the second-opinion appointment—which consisted of a conversation, exam, and basic bloodwork—as if my diagnosis itself wasn't enough of an insult. Angry at the decisions by governments and corporations which have allowed toxins into our waters, soil, air, food, medicines. Angry at the ALS Association for not adequately funding the most promising research on treatments that could have made an immediate difference for patients, but still managing to beg for donations while sitting on millions of ice-bucket dollars and sending their high-salaried executives on luxury vacations.

I was angry at overconfident alternative-healer types who assured me that a hefty investment in their brand of chiropractics, energy work, extreme diet, wonder supplement or meditation would surely provide the magical cure. Angry at those amateurs with far less aggressive conditions who got better and then smugly lectured the rest of us about the simplicity of curing any condition with enough willingness. Angry at the whole class of dirty insinuations tossed toward misfortune: *"Have you considered how you've created your situation for unconscious reasons? At least you're burning off whatever bad karma caused it,"* as if damning assumptions provide shiny examples of a healthy attitude.

I was angry about what people assumed when viewing my disabled body. That once I was a wheelchair user, I had regular run-ins with strangers who would greet me by leaning over and smiling broadly while slowly yelling in my face, "My, aren't... YOU... a pretty... girl!" That they'd complement simple statements like

"I'll email you" by pretending to type on an imaginary keyboard, or "It's cold outside" by rubbing their arms exaggeratedly, in case I no longer understood English and needed the translation into Disabled. That many of them were health professionals, getting paid well for their skills during our encounter.

I was angry that even armed with a graduate education, an organized mind, and ample free time, I could barely grok the byzantine processes of Medicaid and Medicare. Angry that customer-service reps wouldn't accept my computer voice as valid during calls, nor my caregiver's voice by proxy, ensuring the most basic business by phone was now impossible. Angry that these examples only scratched the surface of the barriers those of us with disabilities *still* face in a world which struggles to accommodate.

I was angry at all the healthy people my age or older who weren't having to deal with this wicked disease, and who still had the dubious luxury of taking their future for granted. Angry at friends who'd complain earnestly to me at not being able to get to their favorite exercise class with their busy schedules… or who would come over on an otherwise nice day wanting to lock gazes, hardly noting my levity and insisting I share about at what point I might suicide… or who disappeared completely because they just couldn't deal with my illness. While perhaps not angry at those with treatable conditions still offering a fighting chance at recovery, I was still envious as hell at the good fortune they often didn't recognize they still had, and of anyone going through any crisis which was only temporary—meaning any crisis which didn't viscerally threaten their whole existence.

Even though I didn't believe in God as the Great White Santa Claus Above, I was often angry at Him/Her/Them, along with all Their comrades in every imaginable tradition, in every imagin-able form. The protectors, devas, angels, deities, *suck it*. My spirit guides could mostly go to hell for all I cared, at least until I could fire them in person. And then there was everything and anything tidily platitudinal or feel-good spiritual in nature, i.e. "It's all part of a larger plan," which I simultaneously wanted to embrace in fair consideration and offer the finger. Mostly I was furious at how early life had failed me and death had staked its claim on me.

These realities—these *relationships*—hurt. But while it all felt completely personal, I knew it was completely not personal. After all, while it's easy to feel victimized, as if it was all happening *to* me, I also felt responsible for so much of it: for somehow getting myself into this impossible predicament, and then for not figuring out how to get myself out of it. For being too methodical about treatment, or maybe not methodical enough. For wasting money on interventions or doctors which would prove useless. For falling for all manner of snake oil in my desperate scramble to heal, and for jerking John and others around with me for the ride. Some-times, for not having found the *right* snake oil. Most importantly, for whatever small or large part I might have played to end up in a life where this would happen—even if that only included agreeing to be born human.

Of course I was angry.

Powerlessness begets rage. Getting a terminal diagnosis is a profound violation to anyone's sense of self. Yet once I'd said, "Yes, hello anger, I see you, I feel you, I respect your right to be"—which I did basically every day—the trick for what to do next became the real question. Do I express it, and if so, how? How do I keep its expression clean so the heat doesn't scald the unwitting and its smolder doesn't eat me alive? Which more vulnerable feelings do I need to invite to the table? Most importantly, how do I keep my anger connected to compassion, so I know what I need to fight for and what I need to forgive? And, eventually—how do I carve a self-loving, wise nuance out of all efforts for forgiveness?

—

Though I could have known better, two years into my illness, when my written word had become stronger than my voice, I drafted an email to my father after a predictably strange and hurtful video call. I must have felt emboldened by something—a book on family systems, or correspondence with my therapist, or the realization that I had little left to lose in being honest in this forever-difficult relationship. It was a direct message that more or less said, "Hi. Thanks for our call yesterday. I noticed, though, that you interrupted to make jokes every time I tried to update you on medical stuff, which hurt my feelings because it seemed like you didn't really care about what I had to say, or what's important in my life. If you showed more interest in hearing my brief updates while I still have a voice, that would really mean a lot to me. Thanks! How's the weather? Love Ter."

Now, I didn't particularly *want* to risk the vulnerability of doing this. *Will he abandon me? Will he retaliate? Will I damage him somehow by sharing my feelings and making a request?* I had tried to confront him about hurtful behavior in myriad ways before, which rarely went well and usually got twisted into me feeling compelled to comfort *him*. But though I knew in theory that certain wounded or entitled people will refuse even the most skillful feedback, I thought things were different now, and email would be less threatening; I thought he could rise above old patterns this once to support me during the difficult road I was traveling. Maybe I would get an acknowledgement that I wasn't crazy, he knew he had been hurtful, I didn't deserve it, and he was sorry. *Hey, I can dream, right?*

So I gulped and hit Send.

And this decision must have been wise on some level, since my longstanding acupuncturist Jessika reported significant news the day after I sent that email. After holding my wrist pulses for a long moment, her mouth gaped open in surprise. "Whoa, Teri. Your liver is feeling really strong. Like… stronger than ever. What have you been doing?"

Considering in traditional Chinese medicine the liver is the organ associated with stored anger, she found my email confession compelling. "Keep doing that, Teri!" she said. "You need this kind of improvement. Keep writing those emails!" I felt heartened to know that by saying, "My needs actually matter," my body was hollering a "Hell yeah they do!" in response.

But my father did not appreciate it as much as my liver did. His reply arrived a couple days later, saying essentially, "No, I didn't do what you said. But if I did, it was not my fault, just yours for being hurt by it. You've always been oversensitive. Even when you were a child, I walked on eggshells around you. The weather is good, wish you could visit."

After my own familiar *welp*—and especially when buttressed by a not-small history of therapy—this reply finally gave me enough evidence that it was time to give up on finding the relationship with him I had long wanted. Regardless of any good intentions, he lacked the capability to show up emotionally, or—even more likely—the willingness to get the help he'd need to *grow* the capability. As they say in twelve-step meetings, you can keep going to the hardware store in search of a gallon of milk, but you're always going to come back empty-handed. While I could go to him to discuss the weather, the price of gas, or a good war thriller, I now knew my healing efforts around this relationship would need to be an inside job—meaning I'd make room to acknowledge, respect, and value *myself* with the kind of care I always wanted from a figure who couldn't provide it. And when I wanted emotional support, I needed to go to those people who had the capacity to offer it.

Luckily, I'd long learned that some people *will* actually show up once we've made the bold decision to share our feelings; some people have the maturity to handle direct feedback without centering themselves, gaslighting, or disappearing. They know relationships require ongoing negotiation, and might even appreciate the straightforwardness we show in letting our wishes and needs be known.

When John and I fought—which we most certainly did, punctuated only by him needing to spoon-feed me dinner or wipe my nose—the process of repairing and learning from our arguments only deepened our intimacy. When I told my friend who had been complaining about her exercise classes that her concerns were hard to hear, given how fortunate she appeared to me to have a functional body at all, she replied, "Yeah, that makes sense! I didn't mean to rub it in your face, but I kinda did, huh? I'm sorry! I won't do that again." And she didn't. And we grew closer, even as the outer details of our lives grew even further apart. When I made a formal complaint about one of the nurses who confused me for a deaf six-year-old, his manager thanked me and welcomed the suggestion for better sensitivity training for staff. Whether or not my speaking up will ultimately benefit future patients, at least I can relax into knowing I never again need to be subjected to that particular yelling dude with the stethoscope. *This is a boundary.*

I could have done it all myself, trying to accommodate myself to the reality of others, assuming my anger was simply a reflection of what's wrong with me instead of a reflection of what's right, what's awake, what cares. One way to know we're doing the work is when we're increasingly surrounded by others who can handle the occasional heat and discomfort of honest negotiation that trustworthy relationships must withstand and grow from, as bumbling as these conversations can be. Overall, it helped for me to see that those worth pulling close—the true gems in my life with the skills and heart to hang in and wrestle our way through raw, vulnerable communication—were teaching me I wasn't crazy for having feelings and needs. Just human.

—

But of course, despite all the lessons learned about where to place my relationship energy, I still had old stuff to let go. Especially to let go the cumulative disappointment that had screeched at me from a hundred different angles since the illness began, which, *shocker,* wasn't magically disappearing by ignoring it. And the most important part in working with feelings the size of a galactic fireball, I remembered, was turning to something larger than me and my little human body to hold it.

By this point I was familiar with ceremonial space and ritual. I had taken Buddhist vows, I had taken plant medicine, I had been married. I had lit candles and burned sage and purged my house of non-essentials like a madwoman on New Year's Day to make room for something new in my life. I knew the beauty of performing some symbolic act to honor and witness that which I was ready to welcome, commit to, and that which I wanted to release.

I knew that all any ritual required was a bit of intention, a respect for the symbolic, and preferably some materials from the natural or creative world: water, soil, plants, fire, paint, cloth, breath, words—whatever elements can remind us that there's some bigger alchemical forces accompanying us which we can call on. It didn't have to be fancy, but it did need to be heartfelt. And since I could no longer do a vision fast, I could no longer drop stones in a creek, I could no longer handwrite my resentments and toss them in a fire, I could no longer dig into the soil to bury a letter, I had to get even more creative in my simplicity. And I needed help. In this case, it would involve compost.

So on a Saturday afternoon long after he'd returned from his training, John agreed to join me in our plant room for an impromptu ceremony. I asked him to grab the bag of compost we kept in our freezer and place it on a plate.

Minutes later, John sat the bag on the side table between us. He lit a candle. I said a prayer. He said a prayer. I named all the things I was angry about. John named all the things he was angry about. Amidst the eggshells and lettuce scraps and dead leaves of house plants, we made our offerings. We named anger about the illness and everything we'd lost. We named anger at no one but circumstance itself. We named names. While moving the aggression out of my body, by offering it in prayer, something inside began to clarify. I felt tender for all of us who die from illness, who live with illness, who care for someone with illness, who survive loss, who are made better by heartbreak. And the disappointment slowly, elegantly, undeniably distilled into an aspect underlying it all the whole time: compassion for the mess we're all in.

John wiped my tears with tissues, then threw them in the bag.

Once we felt complete, naming everything we had to name, we each took deep breaths and blew all leftover fighting energy into the bag of compost. Like any good ritual does, I already felt transformed, refreshed, buzzing by a rearranged internal land-scape. A little tired, and thirsty. John took out our heavy compost to the bin. We knew some bigger alchemical force would handle our anger better than our own bodies could, transmute it into an essence capable of nourishing future life. And for our purposes, it already had.

PART IV:

Grace

19.
The Empowered Surrender

SPRING 2019

Nearly a year since our last visit, John and I agreed it was time to return to the dreaded ALS clinic at the Denver hospital. Since no one was learning anything from my silent protest of their depressing approach, and we wanted some practical help, John took the afternoon off work and we trundled down with my manual wheelchair for the ninety minutes I would give the normally-four-hour-affair. We figured this would be just enough time, since by this point we agreed to forgo the "do no harm" do-nothing neurologist, the speech therapist who would not get my voice to return, the doe-eyed occupational therapist, and the dietician who would only tell us to feed me Ensure or another synthetic food-like goo, which I resolved to endure a noble death before surrendering to. I brought typed notes for John to read aloud to the remaining few providers who made the cut.

After a brief meeting with the respiratory therapist, during which she cheered me through blowing into a machine as fast and as long as I could to measure my diaphragm strength, we were ushered next door to meet with the physical medicine doctor. John and I agreed Dr. M was one of the gems of the clinic, a comforting ally in the choppy sea of allopathic medicine. His bedside manner was gentle and respectful, and he took our questions seriously. On this day though, he soon looked disappointed. Grimacing while reviewing my forced vital capacity (FVC) diaphragm capacity test results, he said with a sigh, "I'm sorry to tell you this, but this score is… well… it's quite low."

"Okay," John said, glancing at me. "What does that mean?"

Dr. M proceeded to explain my FVC was just thirty percent of normal, a sixteen-point drop since my last visit. In the world of ALS—or any other world—this signaled significant internal muscle loss. Continuing in an apologetic tone, he explained this meant that I was no longer a candidate for feeding-tube surgery, because my abdominal weakness would make the procedure dangerous.

That's it? I thought, inwardly chuckling, triumphant that the doctor was more upset than I. *Phew!* The idea of a feeding tube, and the requisite hole cut into my stomach to accommodate for one, strangely never excited me.

Prior to this point, I had put myself through many brave ordeals which others strive to avoid. I could take the cheap train alone across India, live in a haunted co-op with twelve ungovernable housemates, dumpster-dive more than furniture, and name the emotional elephants within large groups of convicts, for example.

Messy minds? *Bring them on*, I've said. Messy environments? *Ain't no thing.* But the nitty-gritty inner workings of bodies, and bodily fluids and viscera and vulnerabilities and processes have remained far, far outside my scope of comfort. I'm such a lightweight with all things medical that I once passed out in my college health center during a casual presentation on the ovulatory cycle; even the language of anatomy and physiology was more than I could stomach.

So unsurprisingly, cutting into my body for tubes or procedures and machines which *may* keep me alive a little longer with a progressing degenerative disease just isn't my thing. Tracheostomy surgery and ventilator which would extend my life by breathing for me? *Er, no thanks.* Loud breathing machine which violently forces my lungs to exercise while I drool into a hose? *Hellish. No.* Oxygen hose up my nose at night? *Ummm... maybe someday... if John keeps nagging me about it.* I could admit it's good these options exist for all the people out there who will tolerate a physiologically invasive hassle to live a little longer; I'm just not one of them.

———

But it's remarkable how our human minds can compartmentalize hassles. I was, after all, no stranger to painful (and, some might argue, obscene) treatment efforts, especially if I thought they might facilitate my return to health. I had stopped the live bee-sting treatment by now, unimpressed with the year of piercing efforts which had done little but speed up my motor degeneration. Three nauseating experimental stem-cell injections were behind me, all to no good effect besides lightening our savings account. And my latest attempt at recovering function, via killing the gut full of parasites that I'd unknowingly been hosting for an unknown length of time was not exactly gentle either, but I'll spare the details.

After the ALS clinic, I investigated the one significant treatment option I hadn't yet addressed: dental cavitation surgery. I already had evidence from digital X-rays that the sockets from my wisdom-teeth extractions from twenty years ago were infected, and had learned that no treatment but actual surgery to remove the dead jawbone and kill the infection at the site would address it. This type of surgery had shown improvements in many people with neurological problems, so I emailed the Texas office of the top-rated dental surgeon in the country, who had become a celebrity darling in the Lyme community. Claiming to thoroughly understand the unique factors the chronically ill face, this dentist had made a name for himself treating, in his words, "the Sickest of the Sick." In the email I explained my diagnoses, my history, and my current symptoms, and asked if he thought they could help. The emailed response arrived the next day. "No, we have never seen any improvements in your level of ALS symptoms from doing this surgery. We're sorry and we wish you well."

Ouch. Apparently, despite my tough spirit, I'm already Sicker than even the "Sickest."

———

Early in the illness I learned that some people take issue with the language of battle, as if fighting disease misses the point. They argue for "waging peace" with our bodies, claiming symptoms are just urgent messages that something in our life stream is kinked and needs immediate attention so we can rebalance naturally. This idea is noble theory and sounds impressively evolved; and yet I'd ultimately decide these non-violent resistors are either moderately disassociated, and/or privileged to not be personally facing a debilitating and life-threatening illness. Like a usually-calm cat that you try to force into the suffocating carrier headed somewhere scary, the teeth, growls, and claws are coming out, whether or not she stands a practical chance of escape. I thought back to the vision I'd had in Peru where I saw my illness as a serpent feeding off my life force. My pure animal instinct was to use every weapon I could imagine to fight back.

So the day after getting this non-encouraging email response, I considered pushing against the dentist's implied conclusion that treatment with him would be futile. *Someone will always be the first new success story... why not me?* I considered what it might take to get the experimental surgery anyway; the cost, the logistics of travel, the hope and stress of one more push.

As I sat with this stubborn impulse over the following few days, something tangled inside began to unravel. I knew dropping the fight by this point would be no small change in orientation. Determined from the beginning to make my triumphant return from the underworld of terminal illness despite conventional medicine's utter disinterest in helping, I had been willing to try nearly everything and anything throughout the three years of battle. And I had: I had tweaked my diet in dozens of ways, progressively eliminating various foods and adding highly nutritious wholefood versions of others. I did liver gallbladder flushes, glugging olive oil and lemon juice before bed and lying down with my knees tucked up to my chest, praying for a stone miracle in the morning. I tried dozens of protocols with various wonder supplements, each new combination promising to conquer what the last round had not, until they all ended up stuffed in the ever-expanding supplements cabinet in somber solidarity with the other expensive losers.

Between meals I took bentonite clay or charcoal or compound prescriptions in an attempt to pull the mold toxins from my gut. I sweated through IV glutathione and IV vitamin pushes to bypass my growing nutritional deficiencies, then I sweated in my portable infrared sauna. I ordered prescription antifungals from India since no doctor would prescribe them, which John chopped up and put in my food because I had lost the ability to swallow pills. I got help from caregivers with enemas and castor-oil packs, which rudely violated my Victorian-era modesty. Jessika poked me with endless needles, and despite her gentleness, I'd often yelp as my exposed nerves jumped. Hours later, I'd choke down bitter, sludgy Chinese medicine herbs, grimacing while attempting to remind myself I was healing.

I saw mold doctors who didn't believe in Lyme and Lyme doctors who didn't believe in mold and countless others who didn't believe in either and attributed my symptoms to something else. Over a year, my crooked spine claimed the lives of 914 bees with little to show for their sacrifice. I took eight planes to two other countries to pursue unconventional treatments, each flight finding me weaker than the one before.

There were energetic treatments, reiki, bioresonance. There was tapping, visualization, affirmations, shamanism and endless meditation. Intuitives told me I was "definitely" getting better, or I would never get better because the illness was a soul contract; they told me I had worked too hard serving others throughout lifetimes and needed to learn to be cared for myself, or I had made an ambitious reach in my pre-birth planning. My head spun round and round, and then some of the best mental health professionals in Boulder counseled and coached me toward believing I was, in fact, doing quite enough to pursue healing.

People meditated on my health, performed distance healings, prayed for me. For a year, seven of my friends would come over once a month and sit in a circle and hold hands for a Power of Eight Group, intending in concert for our various needs for healing and strength. I had my own angry prayers, affirmative prayers, desperate prayers, polite prayers, bargaining prayers, sitting on the toilet, not-sure-if-I-could-find-the-energy-to-ever-get-up prayers.

And I got so very tired. Physical exhaustion was a given, but it didn't compare to the emotional and mental fatigue of investing all my hopes, interests, and efforts into failed treatment after failed treatment. All my best efforts had so far barely caused a ripple in my physiological stream, which by this point required a Herculean effort to reroute toward destination non-paralysis. Having already gotten my hopes up a certain number of times in various so-called hero treatments only to see zero or very minimal improvement, it became harder and harder to imagine that my body would respond to anything. It was as if I were digging a tunnel in search of a treasure, but every shovelful caused the ground to get harder. I lost faith and enthusiasm. And I had no idea where to find it again.

Against this backdrop I began to admit there were no reasonable options left for pursuing recovery; that continuing to drag John toward faraway, longshot efforts was unkind, bordering on the absurd; that it was finally time to cease this mad searching, this fighting, this striving, and *let go*. These thoughts pierced through my mind with a hot, searing sting.

Meanwhile, I knew that surrender has a bad rap in certain circles, and is sometimes even viewed as evidence of weak character. Maybe it's a product of a bootstrapping American ethos, or maybe it's simply patriarchy's passionate hunger to conquer. Either way, the victory-at-all-costs mentality takes self-determination to an extreme, like the mindset of an adolescent fueled by surging hormones: "I can do anything! Don't tell me 'No!'" And we all know how well that goes.

Even in chronic-illness communities, the decision to wave the white flag in the face of disease is often portrayed as an embarrassing defeat. Many of my Facebook friends with ALS had carried "Never Surrender!" as a battle cry, even using some version of this sentiment as a signature or profile motto. I got it. After all, I didn't easily accept others' submission to the disease; I had even once been that person urging others to be optimistic in treatments which I later recognized wouldn't have helped.

All I knew at this point was that I no longer wanted the seventy-five potions and powders and protocols, the strict diets, or the treatment projects that preoccupied my caregivers and myself for hours each day. I no longer wanted the never-ending research and discovery of new longshot treatment options or the gargantuan effort to keep producing fresh hope. I no longer wanted to meditate in an effort to improve myself. It all felt futile, sad, desperate. It left me hungry and cynical and spent.

Of course, I had cried uncle before; overwhelmed with grief and frustration, I'd surrendered again and again to the emotional pain of the situation, which usually resulted in a long cry, allowing just enough relief to plow forward with my determined project of changing my fate. But fully surrendering to the inevitability of my progressing disability had an altogether different feel. I realized, if I had worked somewhere between *minimally* and *moderately* hard at getting all the great things in my life, my marriage, education, career, community, recovery, etc., and my efforts had always proven "enough," but working *extremely* hard for physical recovery by pouring everything I had into it and still getting zero results, perhaps recovery wasn't the right goal for me anymore. Not that I didn't deserve it, but maybe I deserved the lesson that comes from surrender and grace even more.

I began to suspect I didn't have to keep fighting where my body seemed to be taking me: further and further from the life I imagined I should be having; further and further from what I had always assumed would be an acceptable destiny. And maybe this was actually an okay thing. Maybe it was safe to wave the white flag. Maybe it was time to redefine what healing would be for me. And if I stopped fighting my physical reality, I could just relax into the freefall, much as that strange download I got a few nights after diagnosis had taught me to do.

So the day after receiving that honest little email with its big implications, I made a decision. I would leave my fate up to something beyond my ego; my own tricks and tools would no longer be in the fight. This decision triggered the psychic pressure valve to start to hiss, allowing the many long months of struggle to slowly deflate. By acknowledging the underworld didn't have to be seen as the ultimate enemy after all, I was finally free to say, "Enough. I'm done fighting. Take me, Death, if you must."

So as this existential exhale slowly unfolded, I decided it was time to revisit the Persephone myth, and why I might have felt her archetypal prescience even before the first conscious tumbling into the underworld of illness. While searching for more information about the myth by pouring through the books and resources I could find online, I was reminded again how subjective the interpretations of ancient myths and folk stories can be. But while the details of the tale varied in every version I found, nearly all I came across seemed to agree upon four essential elements:

1. Persephone had a certain plucky innocence about the dangers of meadows. *Check.*

2. She was initially deeply unhappy with her new location after being abducted underground, cut off from everything she knew. *Check.*

3. She endured a difficult transformative initiation in the darkness of the underworld. *Say again.*

4. With the help of Demeter and Hekate, who represent the strong archetypes of mother and crone, she eventually returned to the bright land of the living in a new, more mature and empowered way, with the caveat of being forever connected to the dark land below. *Well… hmmm.*

This fourth element proved tricky.

What might "returning to the land of the living" mean if I wouldn't be recovering physical functioning? My therapist mind already knew how to broadly fit my journey into the universal themes of maturation and individuation; that much was easy. Clearly, because of the physical facts of the illness, especially of losing the use of my arms and hands, I had been forced to learn how to stay still, rest, and receive help in a prolonged manner. This opportunity invited a certain comfort and eventually even relaxation with being in a role of receptivity and trust, typically the kind of virtues associated with a "feminine" archetype. This was also true for losing my voice; losing it meant I was forced to spend more time reflecting and choosing my words more wisely. And while my relationship with my mother (and everyone in a nurturing role) had certainly matured through the illness, I suspected the "feminine rescuing" was to be seen through a more metaphorical lens, i.e. my own inner feminine—whatever that truly means—and even how I mothered myself. Yikes.

And this is where the decision to surrender the active attempts to control the illness (the "doing") in favor of just allowing and making peace with its existence (the "being") takes on special significance. Ending the fight with the illness in no way meant I was powerless over everything, since surrender is *also* about claiming a truth that we've ignored at our own peril and acknowledging that we may need to embrace some aspect of ourselves or our situation which we previously could not acknowledge or accept. For me this meant acknowledging that I never really wanted to believe that healing would be my reward for white-knuckled pushing; that I didn't want to live in a world so transactional, where only if I was outwardly "good" enough and checked all the right boxes would I get blessed with the reward of a viable body. I realized there was exactly something about having to do everything "right" that was itself in need of healing. "Right" had seemed to work for everything else in my life, but "right" wasn't the answer for this illness.

In fact, this surrender meant that I could reclaim my locus of control from looking outward to inhabiting inward for answers. I now knew no guru could save me. No doctor could save me. No shaman, intuitive, or miracle worker could save me. My own best ideas had not saved me. And focusing on physical treatments, though understandable for a time, distracted me from having to grapple with everything that I still didn't know how to fully grapple with: my pain, my fragility, my rage, my potential, my passion, my desire to belong on this fucking hard but beautiful planet, my desire to be and do *enough* and my fear that I never would. So to mine whatever wisdom I could from this situation, I'd have to turn within to ask the deeper questions I needed—the heart questions. And then I'd have to wait in that deep darkness, the land of emotion and intuitive knowing, listening like I'd never listened before. *My dear sweet self, what seems to be the root problem? Is there truly a problem at all? What will nurture my spirit, and what does my body need now? What do I most need to let go of, and what am I most hungry for? And most importantly, what is the true healing I seek?*

Only from there could I "return" wiser and clearer, more fundamentally *myself*, bearing the gifts from the underworld. And maybe then I'd understand what of me was literally returning to life.

20.
Radical
Revisioning

SUMMER 2019

This decision to stop fighting changed everything and nothing. After a long conversation, John said he understood my fatigue and disillusion, he felt the same way, and though heartbroken, he would support my decision to stop treatments beyond what just comforted me. He cried; I cried. We both exhaled.

I told Chris not to worry about learning my latest detox protocol because I was going to wean off it. I told a few close friends who visited that I was done fighting. I crafted a long email to my family that I couldn't bring myself to send. Beyond that, life hummed forward as it slowly does. I continued to need more and more help with basic tasks. In the daytime I wrote and clucked over Anu, and at night John and I heckled *The Great British Baking Show* and tried to slowly reflect on our changing outlook for my life.

Since I knew my deeply altered physical reality was most likely irrevocable, I identified two broad options for moving forward: 1) A rejection of what I'm left with in whatever time I still have, and a resigned defeat; or 2) A deep revisioning for how my life has transformed and what opportunities I still have despite the losses. Over the course of the illness, I had explored both paths, sometimes flitting back and forth within the span of one afternoon.

This first option, of rejecting my downsized life, was possible in both figurative and literal terms. I could shut down in nihilistic despair, sleep a lot, binge on TV, refuse conversation with God/Source and His/Her/Their henchmen, get lost in self-pity, fight with loved ones. This seemed a decent approach at least for a few hours on some days, since if I focused on what I had already lost, it would be easy to conclude I had no quality of life whatsoever. I was no longer anyone's therapist, teacher, colleague. I could no longer cook a stew, wrap a gift, answer the phone, or go for a walk. I had no arm strength to hug, lip strength to pucker for a kiss, vocal cords with which to laugh aloud. I became less an actor and more the acted upon as the most basic human acts of self-care increasingly relied upon the style, rhythm, and timing of others. Some potpourri of groan-inducing leg spasms, uncontrollable tremors, the dumpy feeling that comes with being slumped in a chair for months on end, random little icepick stabs, monster itches with no way to scratch, pronounced sensitivity to shrill sounds, shortness of breath, and ill-timed outbreaks of uncontrollable laughter became an hourly affair. These realities pointed at a gaping chasm where a certain basic quality of life once rested, the losses real, stunning, growing, and, most importantly, not likely to ever be recovered.

But beyond perpetual moping about the time I had left in the torture chamber known as the pain school, I knew I also had more literal options of rejecting my life. Whenever anyone would post on ALS forums saying "I can't do another day, I'm done," they'd wind up with overflowing responses from sympathetic patients in similar mindsets, all sharing their research and known resources for how to go about initiating their own death. And my clients who had survived incredible ordeals had already taught me that sometimes, knowing suicide is an available option is the mercy that can keep one going for so long in the first place.

By the point I stopped battling where my illness was taking me, I knew Colorado is one of the states which allows people with terminal disease to hasten their own death, courtesy of a carefully prescribed pharmaceutical cocktail. With that, I could type my goodbyes, slurp down one last sugary drink, and quietly fade out over a few hours as my organs shut down like slowly nodding dominoes. Fair enough.

The only problem with this option is the lethal prescription requires proof of ability to self-administer the liquid. While meant to protect vulnerable patients, this law effectively rendered us paralyzed folks ineligible by the time we would most want to use it. We couldn't lift the blasted cup ourselves, let alone swallow quickly enough before coughing half of the necessary elixir out, which would give new meaning to the bardo between life and death.

The other problem with this option is, of course, its finality. Every time I tried to seriously consider the logistics of initiating my own death—whether through a quick drink, or a prolonged process of refusing food and water—something life-loving within objected. I kept finding reason to see the next day, or week, or at least experience the next inhale. And I quickly noticed that every time I made it through another "I-can't-do-one-more-day" day, my outlook would soon enough change. If I gave myself the necessary time to get torn apart by regular tsunamis of grief and angry one-way conversations with the ceiling of my bedroom—to let the feelings *move*, whether alone or supported by others—I discovered something beautiful: my situational depression was totally, mercifully workable.

Having survived the non-stop adaptation and reckoning in the years since the weakening started, I was free to explore what of me might still be left glinting in the rubble of my former life, despite my paralysis and progressive decline, despite everything I'd already had to let go of. And not only what remained glinting, but whether anything new had arisen from the friction of the mounting losses; my Persephone offering.

Of course, these questions of gifts still lost claim to easy answers. Sure, there's the humor I grew; the patience, perspective, dropping unnecessary concerns, appreciation of impermanence, greater spiritual sobriety, *blahdy blah blah*. But even if I *was* growing as a soul, I wavered in the conviction that these shifts were a good-enough trade-off for the use of my voice and limbs in this lifetime. The narratives about guaranteed happy endings had been exposed as fantasy, my agency over my reality much less obvious. I would have to dig even deeper.

Luckily, I had the time. By late summer I had settled into a simple routine, rarely leaving the house except for the odd doctor's appointment or drive through the foothills with John. Whereas my life had once been cluttered with work, exercise, errands, household projects, travel, social events, and generous planning for the future I thought I would surely have, now, my choices became simple. I could nap; I could write; I could sit on the deck and watch the squirrels fight and the grasses sway; I could meditate or read great literature. I could reflect on my ever-kooky and colorful dreams; I could get lost in albums I loved. I could slowly tap out a sparse conversation with a visitor, allowing for deep breaths from both of us. While my eye-gaze computer allowed me to connect to the Internet, with everything that entails, even my surfing somehow felt more interior and spacious.

While artists or devotees sometimes go to great lengths to create situations of solitude to deepen their connection and creativity, my body was essentially creating a solitary retreat for me, forcing me to slow down and beckoning me to listen. I realized if any illness is capable of encouraging introspection, I'd been awarded the most ingenious version, the Royal Emperor of Neurological Disease Which Mercifully Spares the Mind. This meant I still had the ability to question, tease and be teased, learn from my mistakes, choose consciously to approach things differently. I could comfort, counsel, and advocate; I was still a wife, daughter, sister, friend, and ally. I could appreciate myself and everything I'd survived. I could let my heart break further than I ever thought possible. I could reflect on everything unique and yet stunningly ordinary about my human life—my aching, imperfect, exquisite human life, which currently still existed.

I had my memories. I thought of all the motley moments of youth, connecting with grandparents now long gone, the gentle pets who went missing and broke my heart. Learning how to play cards, throw a curveball, cry my way through algebra homework. The dramatic teenage pool parties. The crushes, the first kisses, the sweet boyfriends I'd end up hurting, and the ones who'd end up hurting me. The music: how Run-DMC became Ani DiFranco became Greg Brown became Nick Cave. The dance parties, the dance classes, the dancing alone in all my various bedrooms through all the various years. The best friends for an afternoon or for a decade. The deserts, the rivers, the beaches, the cities which potentiated longing or loneliness, romance or magic.

And all those moments of everyday experience before and after and in between. How I was fully present to many of them and wanted to be nowhere else, losing myself in laughter or joy or sweet, plain nowness. And *also* how, in the midst of many of these preciously ordinary moments I had hungered for what was next, as if the true satisfaction and achievement in my life was held in the distance somewhere, dependent on the proper arrangement of external circumstances: finding the right home in the right town, the right education, the right work, the right love, the right income, the right experience, developing the right skills, or recovering the right body, all the while losing the wrong emotions or habits or hurts. Yet with the fulfillment of each goal the target always moved, taking my hunger and focus in a new direction. And in the process of waiting for my never-ending desires to be actualized and neuroses to be neutralized, I often missed the goodness constantly chirping at my own feet, begging for attention and appreciation, begging to have me rest, look around, and say, "Ahh. For today, this is enough. My life is already enough."

So it was to my delight I would find that marching further into the disablement of my condition would not necessarily mean greater despair. I could relax in contentment instead. In fact, I could even mine some joy while living in suspended animation between worlds. Despite the doctors who called this the worst possible disease, despite the people who claimed they would rather die than experience my fate, one basic truth kept showing itself: My life still had value. It was still, to me, a life worth living.

———

Many months after fully accepting my condition, on one of those rare precious evenings John and I interrupted our routine to verbalize what was working in our lives, we took turns sharing our statements of gratitude. With him lounging on the futon nearby and my face at my speech device, I let my eyes type for a moment on my digital keyboard and then pressed play: "I'm grateful we have lots of natural light in our house. Our plants are booming."

John nodded in agreement. "The fact that we found this house at all is amazing. And we're not living in mold."

I typed, "Yes. And we can communicate through technology that reads my eyes. Incredible."

And our list continued, back and forth.

"Anu was found every time he got out this year."

"We are getting even better at repairing our fights."

"That windstorm last night did not end up blowing a tree into our house after all."

"Our friends are quirky and real and have been incredibly generous."

After a soulful, reverent hour of reflection, we grew tired of earnestness and opted to instead see who would get kicked off the *Baking Show* this week. But if we would have kept going, our gratitude list of marvels could have been long: Hot running water. Kind neighbors. A caregiver I liked, who also liked me. Leftover mushroom casserole in the fridge. A president who hadn't yet started nuclear war, and might not even get to. The ability to see and read and hear. A record player, some good records, and working electricity. The windowsill orchid that John didn't give up on, about to burst into bloom again.

21.
Open-Eyed
Goodbyes

SUMMER–FALL 2019

O n a hot Saturday afternoon a couple months after the discussion of my dwindling options for life extension at the ALS clinic, we had an in-home visit with the local ALS Association representative. There to support us and try to provide resources, she sat on our futon while Anu sniffed her over and explained rather casually that my low FVC score qualified me for hospice. Apparently, my reduced level of diaphragm function made me susceptible to "respiratory events" which suddenly end in death. "Some just go to sleep at night and don't wake up," she said, making it sound peaceful and remarkably uneventful… an *anti-event*. She then seamlessly launched into an argument for the practical benefits of hospice: besides offering free medical services in-home, the hospice staff are prepared to help the family through the practical matters in the hours following death.

This was somewhat shocking news. *Hospice! That's like the End end!* My mother was in town and happened to be sitting on the futon next to the representative as she explained. She struggled to keep her voice steady when whimpering out shaky questions, her face turning red and her eyes glossy with tears. I tried to shove the wrench-to-my-heart feeling aside to be dealt with in a future, more private setting.

But when I put the bigness of the "hospice" label aside, I met with a surprising relief. My death would finally mark a transition out of a challenging physical experience; a long-anticipated graduation of sorts from this occasionally brutal planet into a decidedly breezier realm.

And so it was that I—that *we*—began a new level of reckoning with my approaching death, and the conflicted mess of tenderness and devastation which death demands of us.

———

As it turns out, dying requires a lot of energy. Or—better said— trying to die consciously and comfortably requires a lot of attention, planning, and forethought. Shortly after officially requesting hospice, our home turned into a non-stop circus of healthcare workers. Some brought stethoscopes and blood-pressure machines, poking my ankles for signs of edema and measuring my biceps for signs of weight loss. Some just brought questions about my state of mind, how I was coping, where I was finding joy amidst the dissolution. The result left me feeling a little like a new animal in the petting zoo, with crowds of well-meaning, wide-eyed visitors approaching me with arms outstretched.

By this point of consciously preparing for the transition, I was not afraid of the *event* of death itself. And I was already familiar with the seductive tug of fear surrounding "what's to come," as well as the utter futility of trying to anticipate future experiences in general—in part, because I'd routinely underestimated my own adaptability in the face of challenge, not to mention the often surprising practical support available to meet changing conditions. Yet I still had concerns about the period leading up to death itself: *Will it be painful? Will I lose control of every bodily function for long, and how might we deal with that? How long might I be able to use my speech device to communicate? Will I have enough notice to wrap everything up with everyone important to me?* My new palliative care doctor, sitting in my living room with a gentle, even tone, did the best she could to address the questions within her scope honestly enough to help me feel prepared: "We have pain meds in liquid form so you can swallow easily. The nurses will provide options for your caregivers to best tend to your needs."

This last question, of wrapping things up with loved ones, I knew could only truly be answered by me. When I was younger, I had been the person who sneaks out of the party through the side door without thanking my hosts. Goodbyes felt awkward and filled with ambiguity. How long do you linger, what do you say, should you hug people even if you don't really want to? Will it involve overlong eye contact? What if you forget to thank them for everything, or misstep in suggesting the next time to meet? *Yecchh.* A social minefield ripe for blunder.

But my training in psychotherapy taught me goodbyes were important, and provided necessary reverence and closure to a meeting, a phase, or a relationship. Whereas I found many clients would prefer sending an email to end treatment, I learned to encourage them ahead of time to plan for a few weeks of meetings to explore the rich territory of closing relationships and the mixed feelings it usually entails. Most professed dreading these meetings; nonetheless, by the end of any goodbye group or individual session we were often made gentler and more present with each other by going through with it. The room would reliably become permeated with a soft, calm presence, temporarily arresting whatever defenses we might usually hold. Even in a large roomful of men court ordered to DUI therapy—typically not a warm, gooey, feel-good type of group—up to half of the members might end up fighting back tears at the graduation of a particularly appreciated member. This was always an instructive experience on the vulnerability lying behind even the gruffest exteriors.

So, knowing I had to show up for my death even though I'd rather not, thus came the season of saying goodbyes.

—

In between the endless practical tasks of one summer evening, John gently stated, "I'd like to know what you want for the rest of your life. What do you still want to do? How do you want to spend your time?"

Such big, generous, yet basic questions. It would take an hour of conversation between us for me to clarify my bucket list aloud: see one last outdoor performance of the summer Shakespeare Festival;

lead one last group at the regional psychotherapy conference; watch the blazing oranges and yellows of fall slowly melt into the dull quiet of winter from our deck; eat whatever I damn well please; finish writing my book; say goodbyes to those I love.

It all sounded so neat and clean—tidy, even. I didn't yet know that I'd soon be invited to confront a troubling part of my past in a deeper way.

The first week in October, I opened an email from the board of directors of Reggie's sangha intriguingly titled, "Allegations of Abuse in Dharma Ocean." The email started by acknowledging receipt of an open letter which had been authored and signed by eight previous senior students, which outlined patterns of emotional and spiritual abuse by Reggie and which Dharma Ocean leadership had tolerated and enabled. It pointed to behavior common to "high demand groups," or groups with cult-like characteristics: grooming, questioning and doubt being discouraged, a culture of fear and paranoia, dissent framed as spiritual immaturity, triangulation, verbal abuse, labeling other paths and communities as inferior, etc., *and* how the most damage in this scenario predictably wound up on the shoulders of those with less social power.

After reading the letter as well as the Board's shifty response, I messaged John at work—"Have you read your email? Holy Shit Hitting Fan"—counting the hours until he got home. This was a big deal; these letter writers were formally shining a light on the shadowy underbelly of the dynamics I had witnessed for years but didn't know how to address or fully make sense of.

Now, suddenly, it clicked. Though previously I would have balked at the suggestion that this beautiful community exploring beautiful Buddhist teachings could be a cult; if anything, it's focus on unconditional freedom, human dignity, and basic goodness made it an *anti*-cult in my mind. But I would soon learn the whole allure of charismatic figures and seductive communities is that they effectively tap into powerful teachings on the nature of mind and reality, the kind which easily register as deep truth in the bodies of us seekers. The wisdom and dysfunction are thus intertwined. Once disarmed by the allure of such wisdom, we feel we've found something special, ensuring it's easy to miss our own dissonance and justify any bypassing, manipulation, and hypocrisy of those running the show.

Within the following month, we watched the tight-knit community further splinter between those who could no longer tolerate the rot of hierarchical dynamics or excuse Reggie's behavior, and those who wanted to defend and justify everything. Even for the conflicted group in the middle, conversations became tense with big feelings on all sides; some long-time friends stopped speaking to each other completely, and couples fought.

John and I added our signatures to the letter and sighed with relief that we were on the same page in wanting to officially cut ties. For us, not doing so would equal condoning a system of spiritual abuse, and supporting the unstable and untrustworthy whims of narcissistic behavior at the helm—a dynamic I felt was decidedly wrong, even violent, especially in the context of a spiritual path ostensibly rooted in awareness, egolessness, and compassion.

Within weeks the remaining Board began to split apart, and a few months later, the organization collapsed completely and shuttered its doors for good. Or so we were told; ousted charismatic leaders with devoted followings have a habit of rebranding themselves in new locales.

Of course, many feelings arose for me in the coming months, especially when connecting the dots of my own disturbing experiences to others' stories, and with larger patterns of abuse reported in similar communities. I was embarrassed to have found myself in a community with such unhealthy characteristics; fearful for those friends who seemed caught in a trauma bond with Reggie; ashamed that I had had my own part to play in upholding the dynamic by not trusting my doubts and officially cutting ties sooner; bewildered that something that had once felt so good and true and special was interwoven with the performance of a Buddhist Wizard of Oz; and shocked by those who attacked the letter writers who had pulled back the curtain. With more research I realized it all fit into the particular mashup of Eastern hierarchy with Western individualism, and a strange allowance of behavior that violates Buddhist ethics of 'do no harm' and mirrors the denial, enabling, and lies of alcoholic family systems.

So I had to question myself, and my whole spiritual framework. Had I simply reenacted relational threads of my childhood in my adult spiritual life? I wondered what and who I could trust, knowing that a situation and teacher I once thought trustworthy and inspiring was corrupted by power in fundamental ways. I thought back to my time in Peru and wondered if it was possible that Reggie was the "very powerful being," part of a "dark lineage" responsible for my so-called curse—especially considering I had taken ritual vows with him. And when combined with a never-bigger disillusionment with manifestation narratives—yet another arena I had fallen prey to, even if only in part—I felt embarrassingly foolish.

Most importantly, I wondered where all of this would leave me in saying my goodbyes to my life. What could I still believe in when the world of the sacred—at least as I had so heavily engaged it—was so muddied by human delusion?

———

Because both of our families lived at least a couple of states away, I knew I'd most likely only have one visit left with most of them, and therefore needed to plan for these. So our calendar began filling up. Meanwhile I remained bewildered as to how one says a proper goodbye and has a sense of closure within the parameters of a weekend visit.

My first major goodbye was with John's parents, Will and Grace. Our three days together started out much like any other visit might have; we discussed family, their future plans, the weather in Illinois, the weather in Colorado. We hemmed and hawed over menu ideas, all of us except John too polite to make any bold decisions. We watched a little TV together and weren't terribly surprised to learn that despite their left-leaning politics, they wouldn't chiggle through the genderbending plotline of *Glee* quite as much as John and me.

I would soon learn that in these sorts of visits, the moment in which procrastination is no longer an option would soon arrive. While we might have been poking around at conversation about death for days, the half hour before the final goodbye always seemed to infect the air with a certain heavy crackle, almost as if a lit match would cause an emotional outpouring impossible to contain. This was true with Will and Grace, who had been generous and loving in-laws even before John and I were married. The moment came when it was time to go to bed, their needing to catch an early shuttle to the airport before John and I were up. I had already typed some pre-programmed notes into my speech device, which I glanced at to activate:

"Well, I really appreciate you guys coming to stay with us."

They nodded.

"I'm sad to say goodbye but I know I'll see you on the other side soon enough," I said, giggling, knowing I could acknowledge their advanced age.

They laughed and somberly nodded.

"You've been great parents-in-law to me. Thank you for everything. I love you."

They returned the sentiments, thanking me for loving their son so well.

We were all in tears. Even this very brief, simple goodbye felt unbearable. While I cried harder in front of them than I had anticipated, the real grief poured out after motoring myself into the bedroom, John stroking my head as I sat there sobbing, unable to tone down the volume despite wishing to.

And so it went. Following this was visits with my parents, brother, grandma, aunts, colleagues, out-of-state friends. awayEvery goodbye seemed to have certain elements in common, in varied order: humor, tears, reminiscing, expressions of love, and of gratitude. Each one was a new but dull knife slowly slicing through a warm heart, as if the utter wrongness of moving forward without someone dear creates a sort of cosmic hiccup of confusion and outrage. *Wait, what? You want me to say goodbye to who? Haha, good joke, not gonna happen. You can just shove it, Death.*

Sometimes I was met with encouragements to feel confident it was safe to let go; that, though the one left behind would grieve deeply, they would survive. When unsure if I'd see my mother again at the end of one of her visits, I managed to only type out "I don't want you to go, Mom" before the blur of my tears rendered my eye-gaze device useless for a good ten minutes. She attempted to comfort me. "It's okay, we're okay," then catching herself, and correcting, "Well no, it's not okay… but I'll be okay; you don't have to worry about me."

I appreciated her efforts.

———

Nowhere was the goodbye conflict more pronounced than with John. Some nights as I lay in bed struggling for small sips of air, my lungs weak and spastic, I thought, *Tonight could be the night I stop breathing and just drift away. Would I want that? Should I say yes?* I was faced with a strong pull in opposite directions: on the one hand, release from the increasing heaviness of paralysis, and on the other, more irreplaceable moments with this marvel of a man. Every time I remembered my exit from embodied life would mean a missed opportunity to wake up to him again, hear his bemused chuckle, feel his warm hands, witness another one of his brilliantly crafted metaphors, my answer was a quick and succinct *No.*

He kept proving his loyalty after all, day after laborious day, already so far into the fatigued march of progressive illness. Every morning before work, he faithfully began the ninety-minute routine of transferring me to the wheelchair, to the bathroom, back to the wheelchair. His matter-of-factness about tending to my bodily functions made my embarrassment tolerable. He combed my hair and brushed my teeth and washed my face, and tolerated my disapproving looks toward the first four shirts he suggested I could wear. He fed me special, swallow-safe breakfast, held a cup of water to my lips so I could take tiny sips, and waited patiently during the delayed conversational thread of my typed-out political commentary on the morning news, somehow always knowing who I was reading about when creating new curse words with my robot voice. Making sure I had tissues and the right amount of layers, he kissed me goodbye and went to work, leaving me to Chris, only to return home immediately after work to do the whole thing in reverse.

"How do you do it, John?" I'd ask through my speech device.

He'd chuckle warmly. "What, take care of you? Well… I'm learning I'm more capable than I ever knew. And I just want you to be cared for. You deserve it," he'd say, stroking my face with the back of his hand.

Despite his modesty, I saw the toll the whole thing took on him. His hair was grayer, his back creakier, his optimism dampened by the harsh lessons of our recent years. He had been made weary. And yet he acknowledged a sense of purpose and meaning he hadn't felt before… an opportunity to extend himself through the *verb* of love a hundred times a day. And as I imagine any primary caregiver knows, sometimes life just invites one to give and give and then give some more for the benefit of another. It's as human—and as ancient—as anything. And if the recipient of one's care is as lucky as I've been to grasp the kindness underlying the sacrifice, they'd undoubtedly end up humbled for the better.

———

On the rare fall evenings when John still had spare energy after placing me into bed, he'd prop up some pillows on the headboard behind him and read a couple chapters aloud from whatever book we'd agreed to travel through. I'd lie awake in rapt attention as long as possible, indulging in his melodic voice. In *Love is Stronger Than Death*, Episcopalian priest Cynthia Bourgeault tells the story of her relationship with her beloved, which, to her surprise, only grew stronger and more committed after his death. It was certainly different than when he was embodied, she explained—she couldn't share a cappuccino with him or see the sparkle in his eye—but there was a meaningful and undeniably mutual energetic exchange between her and his essence all the same, and she knew her job was to continue cultivating it.

We discussed this possibility on subsequent mornings once I had my speech device handy again, and I requested John's next partner be willing to engage in an open (soul) relationship. We discussed how the living are still connected to those who've died, even if the living must pay more attention to sense the remaining tendrils of juicy, undulating connection with their disincarnate loved ones than ever before. That maybe love at its most basic is to feel and cherish the invisible thread tying us to that which we love; to work for the spiritual well-being of the other above all; and eventually set them free from our talons that we hope would tether them to us, or to corporeal reality.

By now, I had relinquished most of the worldly tethers to who and what I had once cherished, even if once taken for granted: my career, my voice, my independence, my home, nearly all my possessions which had once held special meaning for me, an in-person relationship with family, my spiritual teacher and community;

and—seemingly—any sense of future in the very body I called home. The grief was real, the loose ends still painfully messy. And yet something was full inside, perhaps fuller than it had ever been. Something had been revisioned; a relaxation, a presence, a reverence for the beauty of small moments. A dropping of the need to be spiritually special. A fuller acknowledgement of *inter*dependence, alongside a never-stronger desire to define my own sense of the sacred. And an awareness of that vital connection with everything life-giving which is eternal and beyond being lost.

22.
The Forest of Forgiveness

D espite the cliché, it's true: there's nothing like being close to death to invite a reckoning with how well you've lived. As the months rolled on in hospice, my decline steady but slow, I found myself taking my own inventory like never before. Could I exit being proud of what I had done with this life? Was I enough of the person I wanted to be—generous, moral, civic-minded—when it most mattered, and when no one was watching? I especially thought about what my mentor Bob had suggested to me four years prior, and what it might mean to forgive myself. Absent all my fancy credentials on paper, absent the books I had read and the meditations I had done, what did I *really* know about compassion anyway?

After a particularly poignant ceremony at the second retreat center in Peru, I found myself on my afternoon video call with John. I often shared the themes of the most recent ayahuasca insights during our daily calls, but this was an especially giddy play-by-play of the prior evening's journey.

"So for a while nothing was happening really, but I got these hints about relationship dynamics, emotions, yadda yadda. Nothing too significant. You know? I didn't yet realize what was happening. That a bridge was slowly building to something big. And then suddenly, I got a hit, like a really, *really* big hit." I paused for dramatic effect.

"Well, are you gonna tell me?" he said, laughing. "What did you see?"

"It wasn't so much a vision as there weren't really images attached. It was just an inner knowing, or... more like a remembering! A remembering that everything is... is just... love. Everything is love. Like, everything."

He paused. "*Everything* everything?"

"Yeah. It's like love is the most essential and intelligent creative energy underlying everything. And we're a part of that love, like agents... or... inseparable aspects of it."

"Okay. Wow." He sat there looking at me through my phone screen, chuckling, taking it in.

I continued, "The whole universe is constantly flirting with itself, and we humans mistake much of the contact as negative or threatening, when in reality it's just an attempt at *us* touching us, since we're not truly separate anyway. Even the seemingly terrible things that happen are invitations to love, in so much as they provide an opportunity to grow. Deep down underneath our confusion and hostility is always attraction; because at our core, we are love itself. In reality we're all just dancing in a cosmic care-fest, a classroom without beginning or ending. I started laughing in ceremony; I couldn't help it. It's just… so… fucking… beautiful."

He was quiet.

Then I told him—with no hint of embarrassment despite the cliché—that I loved him eternally and unconditionally, like a golden thread forever backward and forever forward in time. And again this was less a revelation, more a memory of something I had always known.

At this, he began to tear up. I couldn't tell him it wasn't romantic in the way he might have thought—not fully. It was more that he was also an expression of this brilliant fiery love-bomb of a universe, and it was impossible *not* to love him in the ultimate sense. Or for that matter, everything and everyone else, even if I tried.

———

At the time, this insight about the primacy of love had been a powerful experience. It seemed to have profound implications for healing. It spoke to the type of universal, radical forgiveness popularized by *A Course in Miracles* and hinted at in the Buddhist Dharma, where we're taught to see harm is only an illusion of the separate self and we may "remember" there is *never* anything to grumble over in the first place. We just have to shift our perspective sufficiently, the argument goes, because love is the only truth and everything can serve as a teaching on a soul level.

Now I had a first-hand glimpse of this concept, enough to give me a glowy spiritual hangover which slowly faded over the couple days leading to my head injury. Others who have had similar types of insight have even been rumored to experience physical healing in the process—such as Anita Moorjani's illuminating near-death experience which she credits as the reason she returned from clinical death via lymphoma, fully regaining her health and publishing a wildly popular book.

That's all very good, of course. Just one problem.

As I continued to sober up after the call, I was reminded again that while it's easy to get high on peak experiences and spout profound spiritual truths about "ultimate reality"—especially when psychedelics or meditation-induced cosmic orgasms are involved—it's an entirely different thing to integrate lofty insights into the nitty-gritty of embodied day-to-day life. Holding universal forgiveness as an ideal is tricky business when we're still plagued by the honest complexities of human bodies and drives, defenses and preferences, families and society. If we're not careful, it encourages bypassing, and bypassing allows harmful and unjust dynamics to continue unchallenged. Years prior, one of my Al-Anon sponsors had suggested to me that when you're dancing with someone clumsy or careless, you don't just pray for them, "rise above" or "forgive and forget," and you don't argue away your own reality of soreness. Instead you clearly say, "Ow! Stop stepping on my feet! That hurts!" In this way you honor not only yourself but the precious toes of *their* future dance partners. At the time, it felt like a revelation.

And now, I knew that "dance partners" could be a stand-in for "future meditation students," among a thousand other possibilities. As much as I wanted to dissolve into blissful trust in the Ultimate Great Perfection, I knew I still had reason to be world-weary of some of its human expressions. Forgiveness was complicated, and while possible to find from the ten-thousand-foot view, not always so tidy from ground level where narcissists roam freely. But because of my liminal existence between worlds, the larger question became not so much how to navigate difficult people and relationships I'd already said goodbye to but how to receive them in my heart, for myself.

——

My mother returned for a visit in early March, this time to allow Chris to go on an ill-timed vacation to Mexico. Coronavirus was spreading fast, adding to the concern that this visit with Mom was even more likely to be the last, since if I were exposed to the virus, it would claim my barely functioning lungs in short order. Meanwhile, it was the type of visit where I kept discreetly fighting back tears at the idea that I'd likely never again get to see her unveil the freesias and jasmine she'd cut from her backyard for impromptu arrangements, or eat her legendary enchiladas, or watch her close her eyes and hold her breath in that way she does when engaging a deep conversation.

In the weeks prior to this visit, I had already been swimming through emotional torrents. There was the hurt about family who struggled to engage in meaningful conversation. There was the profound disappointment in Reggie, who was only revealing more unhinged narcissism every time he sent another sangha-wide email in the effort to save his rapidly tanking reputation. There was the hydra of systemic racism, misogyny, and xenophobia permeating the larger culture, along with the maddening disavowal among leaders that these realities still exist. There was the warring political discourse online leading up to the presidential elections which I felt a responsibility to actively participate in, to the detriment of my own sanity. There were the growing cultural disagreements about how seriously to take the threat of the pandemic and what to do about it, while knowing immunocompromised folks like myself stood to lose the most from careless misinformation. And in the midst of it all, I continued to see myself in all my persistent humanness: the blind spots, the biases, the eagerness to blame; in many moments, to identify with the good guys and despise the bad guys, to lump people in categories, to write them off wholesale. Adding to the frustration was how I wasn't even able to wash my own dang hands.

It was against this backdrop, and after Mom had been cooking all day and tending to the never-ending adjustments for comfort which a paralyzed body requires, that she and John sat down with me for a movie after dinner. At her request we chose *A Beautiful Day in the Neighborhood*, in which Tom Hanks portrays children's TV star Mister Rogers, pursued by a cynical investigative reporter hoping to poke a hole in his nice-guy act. The film turned out surprisingly moving, affirming the complexities of emotions we humans have when navigating relationships and passages of life.

By the mid-movie scene which showed the journalist and Fred Rogers sitting down for lunch at a Chinese restaurant, I was thoroughly entranced. With his gentle voice and easy gaze, Hanks-as-Rogers suggested to the journalist—who happened to be carrying long-held resentments against his alcoholic father—that he wasn't left "broken" by his childhood; that he was made prin- cipled in response to his father, and was given an opportunity to learn from his father's choices about the right and wrong ways to treat others. In a nod to ultimate forgiveness, the message seemed to suggest that it's possible to pull something redemptive from much of one's experiences, even if deeply painful. Mister Rogers then invited his new friend—and the audience by extension—to take one full minute to silently reflect on everyone who had loved them "into being."

Following directions, I inhaled another layer of gratitude for all the people who had so far offered large or small kindnesses which affirmed in some way my right to exist on the planet with dignity: the grandparents who had delighted in me, the teachers who had encouraged me and professors who had challenged me, the friends who had picked me up when I fell. There were all the pets who had nuzzled me quietly while I cried, the trees that had held strong against my back when in need of support, the coaches who had cheered me on when I wasn't playing well. The imperfect yet significant care of my mom, dad, and older brother; how so many of the best parts of me grew from them. And despite all lingering confusion and pain, I knew there was deep beauty to so many of the teachings Reggie and my sangha had offered to me; that much of the love I felt in the community was genuine, and meaningful.

As my heart swelled I saw—or, perhaps more importantly, felt—how the small, ignorant, careless, hostile actions of all of us so often need what Matt Kahn deems, "more love, not less," especially if "love" in this case means witnessing, understanding, and offering a path to redemption. I remembered how when making my own amends, something I had learned through the twelve steps, the receiver was almost always gracious, and afterward a rush of heart-opening lightness occurred and relationships occasionally deepened. I thought of how learning to acknowledge my own shadowy behaviors had served to soften many complaints against others, as it became undeniable I had been the perpetrator of various injustices at certain points, as well as the victim: I'd been power hungry; I'd crossed boundaries; I'd said and done my fair share of stupid and hurtful things; I'd abused social privileges without awareness. And I could see how my actions arose from fear or vulnerability, selfishness or ignorance, and the only thing that ever helped me grow up—in addition to being held (and holding myself) accountable for my behavior—was education and acceptance and nurturing from those around me; dare I say, a practical forgiveness.

At the end of the film as the reporter's father lies dying, I thought of my poor health and my father's poor health; of all the painful conflicts I've had over the years with family and friends, contrasted by all the shared love and vulnerability; of the bumbling messes which are human relationships. And something cracked inside. With Mom holding me on one side and John on the other, I cried freely, letting go of another layer of complaints I had carried for so long: the shortcomings of my parents, and the shortcomings that had been handed down to them from their own parents, and their parents' parents. How they had all offered everything they had to offer, swimming as strongly they could through their own currents of generational and social context, trauma and pain, ignorance and confusion, wisdom and grace, like all of us must ultimately do.

And I saw the webs of pain holding so many others whose actions I had struggled with or been hurt by. How Reggie was himself informed by a lineage ripe with abusive power, and how he had acted out unhealthy aspects of power on students in ways not unlike his own guru had done to him. How the doctors who reject patients like me are themselves operating in limited frameworks for addressing health, and how underneath any callousness must lie pain at being impotent in the face of patients desperate for answers. How the men who hurt women are themselves molded by a story of masculinity which cuts them off from the empathetic, relational, humbled parts of themselves, the parts which could ask for help and conditions which could wisely hold them accountable. How even those diehard Trump supporters I encounter, as impossible as it is to forgive the hateful narratives they so often cling to, are largely acting out of their own resentment which deserves to be understood within a much larger context of fear, pain, and separation.

When I could both recognize my own wounds and take the step back to behold the bigger patterns we're all a part of—patterns which have doled out pain and disconnection, abuser and abused, loss and grief throughout time—I felt my heart crack open further to the collective predicament and conditioning holding so much of us captive. I saw how we are all water in the larger ocean of lived experience. I wanted to be transformed by the anger and disappointment, much like the compost ritual had shepherded my internal fire into compassion and the desire for justice; to, as Mister Rogers might suggest, mine it all for unexpected lessons of courage and grace.

———

So even four years after our coffee-shop conversation, my mentor Bob's suggestion to forgive myself first kept unfurling for me as a kind of contemplation. Although after our meeting I had relapsed into determined, sometimes aggressive attempts to "heal" at all costs, I naturally became more ready to integrate his wisdom over time. And by the time I gave up on the plan to recover and had entered hospice, by the time I was thoroughly worn out by *striving* for anything, I could admit he'd been right. The reminder to ease up on myself was appropriate. It was necessary. If forgiveness is showing generosity to each other in the face of our shared humanity and fallibility, it makes sense to at least *try* to start at home. And because I knew the self/other dichotomy is on one level a falsehood, it seemed every movement toward true compassion was a win for not just me but for all.

But what did loving and forgiving myself mean, really? Because while "self-care" makes for good marketing and "love yourself first" is an easy thing to say, the pop culture self-help suggestions for spa time and yoga workshops and daily consumption of coconut kombucha are capitalist versions largely missing the point. While conscious consumption *might* be one expression of self-love, forgiveness is not transactional. And glossing over meaningful details of one's life and history to feel more comfortable and checked-out sure isn't it either.

In quiet moments before John helped me out of bed in the morning, I began to develop the suspicion that true self-love and forgiveness require fierce personal inquiry and accountability. They require getting the help we need to meet our responsibilities to others and ourselves, which might require committed psycho-emotional work for a long, *long* time. They mean engaging our own shadows of unexamined privilege and ignorance while right-sizing our ego. They may be about leaving difficult relationships and situations, or instead seeking out the resources and support we need to stay in and grow through them. And eventually, if we're willing to admit we're worth the ongoing effort of making brave choices and practicing noble behaviors, we learn how to respect ourselves much as we believe a beloved grandparent or growing child or towering oak should be respected. *Because we are also uniquely odd, and irreplaceable, and precious, goshdarnit.*

———

After all those long months, I even began to articulate what to forgive myself for.

Again and again I've reminded myself it's okay that there are still unresolved questions in my heart about my life, and about life in general. That it's okay that I'm leaving this planet without some grandiose self-actualization or specialness, and that my current best understanding of what it means to be "spiritual" is to practice being generous, moral, thoughtful, civically engaged, and willing to roll up my sleeves for the practical work of caring for others; to be an ounce more grown-up than the day before. Immediate to the illness, I can forgive myself for getting sick, and for all my choices and patterns throughout life which *might* have *possibly* contributed to it. For not ultimately piecing together the root causes, and for not undoing it through my own efforts. For not being able to write the triumphant comeback story that everyone wanted.

Forgiving myself means affirming that the "serpent" of illness doesn't need to be rejected by me; it needs a medicine of metaphorical feeding, of careful witnessing, of being regarded as a teacher, even if harsh. Even if the ultimate reason for and result of the whole experience is beyond my ability to comprehend, forgiving myself means accepting the mystery and booting out the tidy notion that there is cosmic justice in life's handouts. It means I could believe instead of "manifesting" my circumstance, I can simply affirm I have been entrusted with an incredible challenge based on an unknowable number of causes and conditions, and am doing everything I can to rise to the occasion and grow through it.

Forgiving myself means reclaiming my dignity by gently releasing the shame of having a debilitating illness. It means humbly standing on the shoulders of those disabled advocates and allies who fought so hard for the rights and tools I now take for granted, and being willing to show up in public in my wheelchair and use my computer voice to claim my unique authority without hesitation. It means knowing I don't need to see failure in my situation; I can claim triumph despite my situation, because I can affirm my inherent liveliness which isn't dependent on anyone else's assessment of my life. And know choosing to affirm such liveliness suggests a well-being more vibrant to any I previously claimed, even when I rode my bike twenty miles a day in my strong, suntanned twenty-year-old body.

And even bigger than the illness, I can forgive myself for the thousand slivers of unworthiness I have worn like tattoos for too long. I can forgive myself for struggling to forgive others and affirm that sometimes, growing pity for certain hurtful figures is the most that should be expected; sometimes, choosing to honor myself is better than spending time forgiving the unforgivable. I can recognize that even those situations and relationships which I look back on as unhealthy were full of nuance, held some beauty, and had value because they made me into who I've become and am still becoming—which is darn strong on the inside even if weak on the outside. That I can affirm, though I still want to grow because evolution doesn't end, I am already enough. This is already enough. I could imagine even Mister Rogers would agree: *I have already been loved into being.*

23.
The Fundamental Safety of Death

SUMMER 2020

By the time it got hot outside again, a full year after my doctor gave me the prognostic sigh of imminent doom, it was becoming increasingly clear that it's not always easy for us humans to accurately predict death's timing. The ALS representative who somberly warned me the previous summer I could die any moment was proven wrong. The palliative care doctor who soon after claimed I "definitely" had less than six months and flashed the hospice nurse an incredulous look for even asking was wrong. My own estimates have repeatedly been extended, to the tune of two to three months at a time. I've now been in hospice over a year, only slightly worse for wear. Month after month my persistent organs keep pumping, or humming, or performing whatever coordinated orchestral magic they're meant to perform.

So while I still have a body, I try to live instead of wait to die. I want to squeeze all the goodness out of this life while I still inhabit it. I try to notice what's working, over and over again: the small kindnesses of people, the delightful oddity of animals, the play of light across the walls. It helps.

Meanwhile, our preparations for my death are laid. John knows that I'm not going to the hospital under any circumstances; that I have no objection to pain medicine; that I want my hands held through the transition. He knows I want to hear his voice giving me permission to let go, that his spontaneous prayers will be heard, and welcome.

We have a plan for the care of my body which feels right and reverential; and when he's ready and my family has gathered—and if pandemic-safe to have one in person—the memorial will be held in a local Unitarian church with big windows and great views. We've arranged to have a local improv troupe perform stories of my life as shared by the audience, so I can go out with style.

We even adopted a sister for Anu—a sassy-mouthed Siamese named Rizzo—to keep the house lively once I'm gone; a small (but not meek) mercy. Beyond that, we've discussed what John's life might look like once I've passed, what will help him grieve, what support he'll need to move forward. John says it'll be friends, family, nature, rest, and lots and lots of time; I'm hoping it eventually involves a sturdy Midwestern woman with a hearty laugh who he adores only an ounce less than me.

I tell myself that day by day, hour by hour, John and my family will find a way to keep going. They will develop new rituals, define their own meaning, continue to forge their own paths; they'll learn to carry the loss one breath at a time. And they'll find a way to squeeze some joy out of the post-Teri life.

———

In between hospice appointments one day and scrolling through Facebook posts, I noticed a number of death-as-enemy sentiments from the metaphysical groups I still belonged to. Some of these posts were from folks writing from their deathbeds, who would claim they knew they could still fully recover if they tried harder to meditate better, or surrendered to faith more, or—despite what struck me as contradiction—commit to do both. Their posts were usually met with hundreds of cheerleading comments: "I believe in you!"; "If you want it enough, your healing is guaranteed!"; "Ask and you shall receive!"

A bit heartbroken over my previously desperate-to-recover self, I opted to offer my own post in one of the bigger groups in hopes it might lighten someone's existential load. So I wrote a little bit about how I'd realized my long-held definition of healing had been confused with cure, informed in part by narrow frameworks which find triumph only in material terms. How the healing I got came in a different package, not through a drug or treatment or meditation which restored my body to functioning, but through a steady saturation of compassion and acceptance from others and increasingly myself which affirmed my wholeness regardless of my flailing body. How it was not until I had surrendered to the full weight of my predicament that I was able to see that finding strength and meaning despite disabling illness was healing. I wrote,

"We're all going to die someday, and it doesn't signal a psychospiritual failure on the part of the dying person. Let's be kind to ourselves and one another. Empowerment is a spiritual virtue, yet so is humility."

The comments and emojis which soon started pouring in were overwhelmingly positive, yet sure enough there were a number of people ready to argue: "Who says we have to die? Some yogis live for hundreds of years." Some wrote earnestly, "All things are possible." There was even the oh-so-smug, "I hope you transcend those views once they no longer serve you."

The lengths of people's denial can be astounding. As my acerbic Christian friend Sam (also living with ALS) liked to remind me, "Everyone wants to go to Heaven, but no one wants to die to get there."

———

Because I didn't shy away from talking and writing about death with anyone who would listen, I occasionally got messages from online friends or acquaintances who were approaching their own deaths and were terrified. Some would acknowledge having long-been dutiful to the scientific materialism which asserts we are bodies and only bodies, that our minds are literally confined merely within our brains, and that physical death therefore signals the ultimate defeat, a transition into never-ending nothingness, the anti-healing. They would peek out of their darkening foxholes to ask me to argue for why they didn't need to be afraid.

Humbled by their vulnerability, in response I'd make some anecdotal arguments about death being another shift in consciousness.

I'd reference the detailed near-death experiences which felt so euphoric that those who had experienced them were hesitant to return to their bodies, and when they did, they were forever changed. I'd mention the story after story of doctors, nurses, or family members who had witnessed the brightness and profundity in the room of a dying person, of how often the dying reach out, calling the names of deceased relatives with joy on their faces. I'd point to the independently verified accounts of past-life details that individuals, sometimes even young children, had no conceivable way of fabricating. I'd argue for how the literature supporting an afterlife spans religious and spiritual outlooks and cultural contexts, and is more than generous.

But it quickly became clear that my skeptical friends would need to cross that river of conception on their own time, if they chose to, and all I or anyone else could do was simply point at the bridge. After exhausting my usual tools of argument, I became lazy, boldly writing things like, "Oh friend. Death isn't the end. It's just not. You're going to just have to take my word on this one until you see for yourself. And you will."

It seems an outrageous thing to claim authority over—an admittedly *tidy* answer—but it was already bone-deep knowing, as obvious a fact as *water is necessary for life*, or *dark chocolate is a good thing.* Upon death, that ever-present witnessing part of us expands, as the egoic veil is left where our bodies lie.

I suppose it could be true, through some confluence of comforting delusion and misinterpreted personal experience, I could be wrong about this. But as someone who has learned to prostrate to doubt, this possibility doesn't keep me up at night.

Us Buddhist-fancying types are good at death, at least in theory. In graduate school, my cohort was required to take a course called Transitions. Meant to familiarize us therapists-in-training with the types of life passages we would soon need to identify in our patients, we ended up getting a crash course in universal (and often underappreciated) varieties of grief. Because my graduate program was big on highlighting the person of the therapist—since it's hard to counsel others if you don't already know yourself well—we had to hold up our own losses to the light. And even as a group of mostly twenty- and thirty-somethings, histories of loss were already there in abundance.

In small groups and assignments, we explored our losses of faith, health, certainty, relationships. Some had already lost careers, marriages, or pregnancies. By the end of the semester, we were made familiar with the idea that life itself is a series of losses, of small deaths leading up to a bigger death. We explored how, far from signaling the end of our existence, these deaths had eventually provided room for rebirths and evolutions in identity, wisdom, or purpose; by some miracle of time and grace, we'd emerged from brokenness to weave together new life.

As I sit facing my own death a short fifteen years after that class, I wonder why so many assume this basic, primordial pattern of transformation ceases upon our own physical death. With generous opportunities to read and philosophize, I stumbled into new questions. *Might we know more about how to die than we anticipate? What if the very design of death itself is already built into living organisms, like babies who know how to head for the birth canal?* Death and birth have certain similarities: they are both monumental transitions, both hold likelihoods for uncertainty, fear, and pain; neither are particularly glamorous, nor tidy. Yet, just as a baby knows how to push toward the light, I imagine that the dying person could locate some knowing function escorting them toward the exit; a knowing equipped to make the passage, perhaps on both instinctual, biological levels and on the timeless, soul level. Maybe some type of midwifery appears to ease the passage. Perhaps we're soon placed in the loving embrace of someone familiar and warm who's been eagerly awaiting our arrival, tears of joy in their cosmic gaze.

If it's true that Earth itself is a school—whether it be a school of pain, or acceptance, or maybe even of courageous heart—that would mean death is a certain graduation. Upon death, we stride across the vast, star-strewn stage to receive our hard-earned diplomas signifying the course of study in which we (hopefully) gained proficiency. But I remind myself graduating from one school hardly signals an end to one's existence, so much as concluding a chapter; that it's not uncommon to have a party after graduation, followed by a good long nap; that one may travel for a while to visit family and old friends, or just to explore, gain perspective, and clarify next steps. Eventually, it seems graduates have two basic options: go back for more advanced schooling even better suited for our needs or find a vocation for which we are now qualified.

These ideas comfort me. I don't know if I'm getting the details right or not. There will always be an element of mystery around death, perhaps rightly so.

Absent all speculation, the contemplation on everything known and unknown, there's always an invitation to listen. We could even cease the meaning-making and surrender to the mystery. Be willing to feel the grief, not just for our own losses but for the big losses throughout time. We could exhale heartbreak for the death of mothers and children, grandparents and lovers, tribes and democracies. The crack of falling redwoods and splitting glaciers, the disappearance of the monarchs and the mourning of the giant tortoise. The landslides, the floods, the fires. We could feel the destruction of mountains, comets, galaxies. All the losses without redemption. All that has been broken.

And in that silence between breaths we could pause. We could acknowledge... absence. In the liminal space we could feel the emptiness. Behold the big, spacious silence behind all noise.

And there, right there, at the edges or perhaps smack in the middle of our awareness we might feel a fullness. The nearness of something sacred, the quiet presence which can't be captured in words—only felt. That which is deeply personal and undeniably universal, that which is me and yet everything not-me, that nearness some people call Source, God, the Great Mother, the Great Perfection, that which can't be named. And as we inhale, we can breathe in all of it, the richness of seas, the quiet dignity of deserts, the opalescent sheen of babies just born. The melody of a downpour and the clarion birdsong as the earth begins to dry. The warm symphonies of stars and the roar of everyone laughing at once. All the beauty beyond description. The truth that everything terrible exists alongside everything miraculous, that loss gives way for finding, and through it all, only love keeps us fighting for what's right.

Closing
Thoughts:
Mining the Jewels

While sitting in a circle of friends in my living room one afternoon deep into the reaches of my illness, my dear friend Cora broke from her usual witty sarcasm to make us an earnest offering:

> It's as if when we're born we're presented with this enormous pile of presents. Some are big, some are small, but all are wrapped so they conceal what's inside. Our task through our lifetime is to gradually unwrap them all in the order they're handed to us. Sometimes we don't like the packaging—some gifts might be wrapped in ugly colors or patterns or assembled by seemingly clumsy hands. But we have the invitation to uncover the gift underneath. Even though it might be tedious, tiring, or painful to do so, we can emerge carrying reverence for what we've learned.

A warm chorus of "uh huh" and "mmm" and "preach" oozed from our nodding heads. Her analogy felt good, especially after we all felt prayer-gooey and the dark chocolate had been passed around. In context of the group's purpose of sharing visions for each other's healing and claiming our desires to grow beyond too-small stories for our lives, it made sense.

But as I reflect now, August 2020, while the pandemic continues to claim so many in needless death and is disabling so many others, mirroring demographics of racial and economic injustice, it's clearer than ever the concept of gifts coming out of loss and illness leaves so many questions. Even if the promises of hidden blessings provide some comfort, the idea itself deserves incredible care and nuance, and is probably best left up to each survivor to decide how much—and when, if ever—it's worth embracing.

Loss itself is not a gift; loss is just loss. Pain is not okay just because we can grow from it. We never need to be blown apart just because we can learn from the act of piecing ourselves back together newly humbled. And being able to mine meaning does not necessarily make it all worth it. When something as precious as our own health or the health of someone we love is snatched away, we might not ever find the necessary spin to see a bright side; we might not ever identify a happy ending.

It seems the more permission we give ourselves and each other to have all the feelings and questions—without offering tidy answers to shunt the process—the more empowering it'll feel to define our own meaning, in our own time, as best we care to. We may remember loss is also old as time, and we are born into vulnerable bodies, loved by and loving creatures also in vulnerable bodies. Humaning was never built for the faint of heart.

But if heartbreak is a given, so is resilience. Sometimes just *enduring* itself is meaningful, affirming that we can keep going even when life has us in a headlock and our whole being whimpers in resistance. We can dig down to find the corner of our body which feels the least like screaming, and inhale every ounce of warmth and workability we can find there toward the other tight corners. The more we can rest in our vast, broken-open heart without flinching—and the more we can cherish the body we have no matter how limp or exhausted or disfigured—the more equipped we are to inhabit the life we've been entrusted with courage.

We can focus on the helpers—they are always there. They can be found wiping our brows or handing us our food or raising hell for our dignity, whispering to us from the past in poetry or from the future in dreams: *Keep going. There is beauty yet.* They have two legs or four, or none, and they accept our shy hugs while staying deeply rooted in the Earth. Fragility invites radical caregiving, and care itself may just be the real currency that makes this interdependent world keep humming.

We can become a helper ourselves, in whatever way our circumstances allow. While we can't take each other's pain away, we can hold space for each other to bear it, nodding at each other's rage and listening to each other's silence. We can honor dismay enough to give it the room it needs without turning away in numb distraction, even allowing our own tears to pool in good company. By saying yes to the guttedness *and* the great love, we may remember they are inseparable.

Eventually we can gather together the lessons learned in survival and share them with others—even if it's simply a quiet internal mercy for everyone who feels similarly broken. In this way we may weave our pain into a tapestry that warms others, or protects them, or companions them. In this way we allow something meaningful to arise, and in doing so we *make* the damn jewels.

And that, friends, may just be the real miracle.

Afterword

Does anyone imagine becoming an expert on chronic illness and the losses it brings about? Fairy, firefighter, athlete, actor, doctor, singer—we fantasize about who we might become in a major key, in archetypal registers. We aspire to do good things, enjoy good experiences and relationships. Wonderfully so.

Life also has its changes into minor keys. Teri tells the story of her downward trajectory into other archetypes; of a different kind of making it through. Her book is in part about what this kind of story and its possibilities might be—not just for Teri but for the rest of us.

One possibility: amidst having her life upended and the last things in her pockets shaken out—tricks, hopes for recovery, able-bodied freedoms—she was still becoming. Indeed, she *found* ways to still become.

Teri's becoming a writer was perhaps augmented by her coming to rely on her eye-gaze speech device to communicate. The voice was hers, in content and attitude, yet it arrived unexpected in pace, rhythm, and coloration. Teri quickly put into effect punctuation to get us to listen up. It was often wry and funny. I think she says surprising things in this book. However, up to the last, at times she would doubt what she was writing, or that she was at all—"It's just obvious, isn't it, what I'm saying?" and, "Who needs to read what I'm going through?"

Is it worth it? We have our own versions of this question. The writing process itself forces questions. Do I say this or that? This way or that? Do I leave this in or out? Teri worried these questions like a river stone. The foreshortening of time by a chronic illness that is fatal had its way. However, she was left time to ponder, reflect, disassemble, sift.

Teri had been musing about writing a book before she became sick. After the shock of diagnosis, she came to a reckoning about how her life might end up. It was in this phase—of acceptance that she was very sick and reflection on what she might do—that the idea of writing a book became possible for her. Possibility became probability after accumulating the PhD's worth of information on the collection of diagnosed illnesses she held. Teri's writing took precedence. Like a dam breaking the words streamed out. She wrote a draft of a chapter, the one on anger, in a day. Boom. Anger into clarity. Stunning.

The experiences did not stop; nor did her reflections. When she was nearly finished editing and the plan for publishing was to begin, she noted, "The changes happen so quickly, I can't keep up. I want to write about it all." She realized that it took writing the book to feel that she was "ready" to write the book.

More was asked of each of us as time spooled on. I too was startled, shocked, and altered beyond belief following her diagnosis. I felt lost, confused, sad, afraid, angry. The losses and the grief mounted as challenges appeared. There were financial burdens, although we were incredibly fortunate to have such generous family, friends, and unknown benefactors whose donations kept us out of debt and bankruptcy. The physical weight was heavy—caregiving is a "full contact sport" and I found it to be rife with repetitive movement injuries to heal later.

There was the ever-present attempt to keep up with the inevitable changes in what needed to be faced and what needed to be done, and I nearly always felt like I was not keeping up. Our situation seemed to me both too fast and painfully slow; enough time to be felt sharply and registered, yet tasks and experience piled up nonetheless. Without much of a structure, a way of seeing the whole, the details were easy to get lost in—like ocean gyres—and I found myself feeling confused more often. Reeling. I would find myself suddenly seeing the pile (as if it wasn't there moments before), feeling hopeless.

And yet Teri and I were drawn closer. I was getting to know her more fully. I found out how she wanted her hair clipped back; how she wanted to be arranged in her chair and in bed. I began to ascertain what she wanted in the moment and be a step or two ahead instead of just passively waiting for direction, and to not feel too bad when I was off base. More importantly, I became more intimate with her as a whole person—what was important to her, what she made of her experience, and what she wanted in her time left. When I could see through the fog of grief, I saw we had the kind of intimate partnership I had always wanted. It looked quite different than how I imagined it, but there it was.

At first, Teri simply told me about what she was writing. She began showing me bits and pieces, and then had me read whole chapters. By fall of 2019 she had an entire rough draft—120K words; enough for nearly two books!—and she wanted me to give her my notes. I enjoyed reading her writing. It was mordant and alive and, again, often unexpectedly funny.

At times we were further apart. Her in her experience and me in mine. As she journeyed into the wilderness, I read her "reports from the field" like letters from a beloved on the front lines of a war. I knew her story, the overall arc, and the particulars, or thought I did. She showed me that I did not. She was coming undone. And becoming. Less inhibited. Funnier than she had ever shown. Freer, even for the bad stuff. Teri was imagining the best way she could navigate through the forest shadows, the blind alleys, and the vast vistas of what remained of her life. That way became by speaking the unspeakable. Teri did so and began proclaiming it more and more proudly. This was such a strange treat, to get to know my wife through reading her.

The book was a microcosm of that experience of something so big, impossible to take in all at once. The volume of what she wrote certainly was, and what she was grappling with in her writing felt so too. I felt lost in it—in my memories, my grief, my own experience all over again. Then *I* was falling. I could not read many chapters without stopping to cry, putting the text aside and pacing, before going back to reading. It was painful. And useful. It helped me stop being absorbed in tasks long enough to feel (and thank goodness for both—to be as absorbed in them as I was, and to have her writing call me out of that absorption). It afforded me the chance to be where I was at, or where I was at the time that the stories had occurred. This was challenging, and I needed it. Helping Teri with her book, in whatever way I could, gave me ways to sit down with myself as much as with her.

I needed to get my bearings. So I offered to go through again and make a reverse outline. I reread chapter by chapter and noted the major threads and anecdotes that brought the story to light, writing them down "old-school" style on 6x9 notecards. I showed them to her and we decided to post them on a stretch of wall in our bedroom so that she, and I, could see the book as a whole. We were able to see the overarching themes through this process and it helped to ask the question, "What is this book about?"

As she moved into the editing process, I began realizing that her journey, through the writing, was helping me know my own. I enjoyed hearing of her victories—her learning the eye-gaze navigation system; her deciding on an outline and a table of contents, and the regular reconfiguring of them; her writing chapters and reimagining them. Seeing her victories helped me recognize my own. For me the book and her becoming a writer came to be a star to reckon by. Even though it felt like I was often still lost in my own wilderness, it helped me to have some vast view from above to map out the territory below. I certainly wanted things—life—to be knowable, relatable, familiar, though "navigating by stars" was not always any of those things. It was not tidy, to use Teri's image and theme from this book. Questions led to more lines of inquiry, rather than to closed, complete answers.

Dealing with uncertainty—not knowing if Teri could be helped or cured physically, and if not, how the disease would progress, how long she had remaining—was a fundamental basis of the pain and challenge for me. This was a part of feeling lost, the reeling. Reading her, especially the themes of clinging to "tidiness" and "hunger," helped me to recognize and name my experience of an existential dilemma. I simultaneously wanted to close out on things—end the uncertainty—and could not be more loath to have it foreclosed. The very certainty I wanted brought with it the image of a final resting place, the fact of death. It felt too cold, too matter of fact. It left things out, things I hungered for; it was too tidy. Teri's death over the horizon was different than having it come into view. Especially when it appeared too close at hand.

Teri lost use of her hands. She lost use of her voice. She lost the ability to walk without support, first with a walker, then with the manual wheelchair pushed by me or someone else, finally with the electric wheelchair. I had more and more responsibility. I saw Teri going from an able-bodied person to someone disabled physically, from a working psychotherapist to someone unable to work in a job out in the world, to someone writing a book and not just that but becoming a writer. I was becoming Teri's "right-hand man" (her left hand too). I was becoming a primary caretaker. I was becoming more competent that I had ever known I could be and developed more capacity than I thought possible. I could do things reasonably well the great majority of the time. (Not always, however, and I had some notable and regrettable failures along the way.) I was doing what I could. I was finding that recognizing this was helpful to *me* too.

Despite all the time and energy that caretaking took up, new habits emerged. I made a hobby of tending our growing collection of houseplants. I felt particularly glad and inspired when I nurtured two orchids into reblooming, a nearly year-long project. What a delight! I remembered new life could flourish around us.

I came to know that what I wanted were ways through the wilderness rather than final destinations. Teri's transformation, her becoming, helped me configure and arrange myself around the vision of going somewhere and getting something done without having to know where I would ultimately end up, without finalizing anything. Over time, I could see that I, too, was transforming.

I was becoming a better husband, friend, sibling, and son. I was not particularly good at asking for help, and not very good at receiving it when it did come. But if any situation could corner me into practicing ways of being in connection with others, we certainly had it. I made efforts to move toward rather than shrink away, becoming more willing to do so without assurance of what might come or how it would work out. I was becoming more flexible in some ways—able to and interested in switching back and forth between roles more readily and with less effort. Never good at multitasking, I became more comfortable with it and less sure that sticking to one task for longer periods was the "right" way about things. In fact, I wrote this in small chunks, often only ten to fifteen minutes at a time.

This process, mirroring Teri's, came to be a different sort of resting place for me—resting into becoming rather than having arrived finally, in total. I am entirely grateful to have done this with her. To have been taught and learned (as much as I have so far) how to become. I say this with the knowledge that it may make it sound like it was worth it. I cannot say that. And yet I would not trade it either. To have had this time attempting to make sense feels good and worthwhile. I've grown better at making sense of this, even though it still does not make much sense after all.

With that said, one last thing—Teri and I came to share a joke—"I couldn't have done this without you." I would argue that's true of anything important.

Echoing Teri's own words, this book could not have been done without many others—family, friends, mentors, therapists, caregivers, cats, plants, dreams—including and especially you, the reader. My wish is that you have found, through reading, ways to your own gifts and to your own transformation.

John Wagner
September 2020

Notes

Epigraph

1. Hobart M. King. "How Do Diamonds Form?"
   https://geology.com/articles/diamonds-from-coal/
   Accessed September 7, 2020.

2. Viktor E. Frankl. (2006). *Man's Search for Meaning*.
   Boston: Beacon Press.

Acknowledgements

One rarely endures an incredible ordeal alone, and this was especially true in my case. Nearly all the lessons and blessings I was gifted with throughout this journey were harvested while others held me literally, energetically, financially, and logistically in a spiral of loving support. This allowed me to focus on the challenging inner work necessary to write and gave me the endurance to keep going when I would rather have given up. For all of you who supported John or me during this challenging time, please know that if I fail to acknowledge you here, my gratitude still overflows.

For my clinical mentors, supervisors, and therapists, who have encouraged and offered gentle perspective throughout (especially Celia Bockhoff); my dearest friends who consistently showed up to share tears, pie, and peals of laughter; and the companionship of my ancestors and unseen helpers, the big trees and four-leggeds.

For the generous spiritual, emotional, logistical, and financial carrying of the Wagner family, especially including Will, Grace, James, Tom, Mari, and Becca. For Debbie, my biggest cheerleader and persevering caregiver, and the warm support of Jerry, Rob, Sawyer, Betty, Melody, Shelli, and the rest of my good-hearted family. Chris Wolfman, this includes you.

For all the PALS and CALS out there showing how far the human spirit can stretch to meet an unimaginable challenge, and who take the time to share with others what they've learned; especially Deborah Wot, the late Rachel Danke-Rebman, Nancy Creek Dolan, the late Karen Potter Stone, and Lindsay Abromaitis-Smith. For all who have fought to ensure dignity for those of us with disabilities; I could not have written this book, let alone gotten help scratching my nose, without having access to eye-gaze technology allowing me to communicate.

For my cheer squad of volunteer editors, including Kevagne Kalisch, Merryl Rothaus, Susan Nimmanheminda, Rebecca Uli, Sakura Gardiner, Jake LaBotz, and RayAnn Gordon. Christina Thiele, you are a delightful designer to work with. Kelly Notaras and kn literary provided on-point technical support and encouragement each step of the way. Chandika Devi, editorial sorceress, and proofreader extraordinaire Laura Kincaid, if there is such a thing as a writer's heart salute, you have mine a thousand times over.

And John Wagner, husband, caregiver, colleague, best friend, teacher, mischievous soul co-conspirator. You made the gifts of this story possible; may my ocean of gratitude, admiration, and love be reflected in these pages.

About the Author

Teri A. Dillion is a licensed psychotherapist, addictions counselor, and clinical supervisor. As an award-winning group process leader, she taught large group process in Naropa University's Contemplative Psychotherapy program and has presented at regional conferences on group dynamics and leadership. In retirement, she now explores what an ethical, dogma-free, engaged life looks like once spiritual bypassing has lost its luster. This exploration includes the humbling lessons of her own early-onset neurodegenerative illness, which she excavates through writing, robust humor, and a hard-won trust in human resilience. She lives in Boulder, Colorado with her husband and two cats. For more info, please visit www.teridillion.com.

Leave a Review

Did you enjoy this book? If so, gather good karma, cosmic high fives, and metaphorical chocolate by leaving a review on Amazon and Goodreads. Thanks so much!

Printed in the USA
CPSIA information can be obtained
at www.ICGtesting.com
CBHW031020311024
16683CB00043B/276